A CARNIVAL OF
MODERN
HUMOR

A CARNIVAL OF
MODERN HUMOR

EDITED BY

P. G. WODEHOUSE
AND
SCOTT MEREDITH

DELACORTE PRESS / NEW YORK

ACKNOWLEDGEMENTS

THE EDITORS wish to thank the following authors, publishers, and representatives for their courtesy in granting permission to reprint the selections included in this anthology:

"The Ballet Visits the Splendide's Magician" by Ludwig Bemelmans: Copyright 1940, 1941 by Ludwig Bemelmans. From *Hotel Splendide* by Ludwig Bemelmans. Reprinted by permission of The Viking Press, Inc.

"Ladies' Wild" by Robert Benchley: Copyright 1938 by Robert C. Benchley. From *The Benchley Roundup* edited by Nathaniel Benchley. Reprinted by permission of Harper and Row, Publishers.

"Shaggy-Dog Stories" by Bennett Cerf: Copyright 1945 by Bennett Cerf. From *Try and Stop Me* by Bennett Cerf. Reprinted by permission of the author.

"An Ape about the House" by Arthur C. Clarke: Copyright © 1962 by The Mystery Publishing Company. Reprinted by permission of the author and his agents, Scott Meredith Literary Agency, Inc.

"Confessions of a Gallomaniac" by Frank Moore Colby: Copyright 1921 by Dodd, Mead and Company. From *The Margin of Hesitation* by Frank Moore Colby. Reprinted by permission of Dodd, Mead and Company.

"Double That Order!" by Parke Cummings: Copyright © 1950 by The Rotarians. Reprinted by permission of the author.

"Father Has Trouble with the Land of Egypt" by Clarence Day: Copyright 1934 by Clarence Day, renewed 1962 by Katherine B. Day. From *Life with Father* by Clarence Day. Reprinted by permission of Alfred A. Knopf, Inc.

"The Indomitable Duck" by Charles G. Finney: Copyright © 1953 by Charles G. Finney. From *Past the End of the Pavement* by Charles G. Finney. Reprinted by permission of the author.

"Who Was Joe Miller?" by Robert O. Foote: Copyright © 1941 by Esquire, Inc. Reprinted by permission of *Esquire* Magazine.

ACKNOWLEDGMENTS

"The Free Lance" by Wolcott Gibbs: Copyright 1934 by Wolcott Gibbs. From *Bed of Neuroses* by Wolcott Gibbs. Reprinted by permission of Dodd, Mead and Company.

"Mary, Queen of Scots" by Guy Gilpatric: Copyright 1929, 1930, 1931 by Guy Gilpatric. From *Scotch and Water* by Guy Gilpatric. Reprinted by permission of Dodd, Mead and Company.

"Nonsense!" by Jack Goodman and Albert Rice: Copyright 1935, 1963 by Simon and Schuster, Inc. From *I Wish I'd Said That!* by Jack Goodman and Albert Rice. Reprinted by permission of Albert R. Leventhal.

"The Deaf Adder" by Colin Howard: Copyright 1953 by Bradbury, Agnew and Company. Originally published in *Punch* Magazine. Reprinted by permission of the Ben Roth Agency.

"The Birthday Party" by Evan Hunter: Copyright © 1965 by HMH Publishing Company, Inc., copyright © 1966 by Evan Hunter. Reprinted by permission of *Playboy* Magazine, the author, and the author's agents, Scott Meredith Literary Agency, Inc.

"You're All Wet!" by William Johnston: Copyright © 1965 by The Diners' Club, Inc. Reprinted by permission of *The Diners' Club* Magazine, the author, and the author's agents, Scott Meredith Literary Agency, Inc.

"A Blow for Freedom" by Eric Keown: Copyright 1953 by Bradbury, Agnew and Company. Originally published in *Punch* Magazine. Reprinted by permission of the Ben Roth Agency.

"One Half of Two on the Aisle" by Jean Kerr: Copyright © 1955 by Jean Kerr. From *Please Don't Eat the Daisies* by Jean Kerr. Reprinted by permission of Doubleday and Company, Inc.

"Pink Ties" by Alexander King: Copyright © 1958 by Alexander King. From *Mine Enemy Grows Older* by Alexander King. Reprinted by permission of Simon and Schuster, Inc.

"Chocolate for the Woodwork" by Arthur Kober: Copyright 1941 by Arthur Kober. From *My Dear Bella* by Arthur Kober. Reprinted by permission of the author and the author's agents, the Robert Lantz Agency.

"The Girl with the Bear Rug Eyes" by Rex Lardner: Copyright © 1960 by HMH Publishing Co., Inc. Reprinted by permission of *Playboy* Magazine, the author, and the author's agents, Scott Meredith Literary Agency, Inc.

"Maddened by Mystery: Or, The Defective Detective" by Stephen Leacock: Copyright 1930 by Dodd, Mead and Company. From *Non-*

ACKNOWLEDGMENTS

sense Novels by Stephen Leacock. Reprinted by permission of Dodd, Mead and Company.

"Man Here Keeps Getting Arrested All the Time" by John McNulty: Copyright 1946 by The New Yorker, Inc.

"How to Play Company Politics" by Shepherd Mead: Copyright © 1952 by Shepherd Mead. From *How to Succeed in Business Without Really Trying* by Shepherd Mead. Reprinted by permission of Simon and Schuster, Inc., the author, and the author's agents, Scott Meredith Literary Agency, Inc.

"Impresario on the Lam" by S. J. Perelman: Copyright © 1942, 1952, 1954, 1955, 1957, 1958, 1959, 1960, 1961 by S. J. Perelman. From *The Rising Gorge* by S. J. Perelman. Reprinted by permission of Simon and Schuster, Inc.

"Money Talks" by Ellery Queen: Copyright 1949, 1950, 1951, 1954 by Ellery Queen. From *Q.B.I.: Queen's Bureau of Investigation* by Ellery Queen. Reprinted by permission of the authors and the authors' agents, Scott Meredith Literary Agency, Inc.

"A Funny Thing Happened on the Way to the Theatre" by Billy Rose: Copyright 1946 by Glenmore Productions, Inc. From *Wine, Women and Words* by Billy Rose. Reprinted by permission of the author.

"The Etiquette of Engagements and Weddings" by Donald Ogden Stewart: Copyright 1922 by George H. Doran Company. From *Perfect Behavior* by Donald Ogden Stewart. Reprinted by permission of Doubleday and Company, Inc.

"The Cliché Expert Testifies on the Drama" by Frank Sullivan: Copyright 1946, 1948, 1949, 1950, 1951, 1952, 1953 by Frank Sullivan. From *The Night the Old Nostalgia Burned Down* by Frank Sullivan. Reprinted by permission of the author.

"The Private Life of Mr. Bidwell" by James Thurber: Copyright © 1935 by James Thurber, copyright © 1963 by Helen W. Thurber and Rosemary Thurber Sauers. From *The Middle-Aged Man on the Flying Trapeze* by James Thurber, published by Harper and Row. Reprinted by permission of Helen W. Thurber.

"Sonny Boy" by P. G. Wodehouse: Copyright 1925, 1926, 1928, 1931, 1937, 1939, 1940, 1953, 1954, 1959, 1965 by Pelham Grenville Wodehouse. From *Eggs, Beans and Crumpets* by P. G. Wodehouse. Reprinted by permission of the author and the author's agents, Scott Meredith Literary Agency, Inc.

TO DON FINE

CONTENTS

CONTENTS

CONTENTS

A CARNIVAL OF
MODERN
HUMOR

INTRODUCTION

The humorist today is certainly not the man most likely to succeed. He is like the dove sent out from the Ark which could find no parking place. Editors look askance at him and publishers view him with concern.

It was not so in the 1920s. In quantity and quality American humor led the world. You couldn't throw a brick in Times Square —not, of course, that one ever did—without hitting a whimsical novelist or writer of what Thurber calls short nervous pieces. We had George Ade, Robert Benchley, Will Cuppy, Clarence Day, Will Rogers, Frank Sullivan, Oliver Herford, Ring Lardner, Don Marquis, F. P. Adams, Irvin Cobb, Harry Leon Wilson, Thorne Smith, and a thousand more. Life was one long giggle.

In these gray modern times you hardly see a funny story in the magazines, and in the theater it is even worse. Playwrights nowadays are writing nothing but that grim, stark stuff, and as about ten out of every twelve plays produced perish in awful agonies, I don't think they have the right idea. If only the boys would stop being so frightfully powerful and significant and give us a little comedy occasionally, everything would get much brighter. I am all for incest and tortured souls in moderation, but a good laugh from time to time never hurt anybody.

And nobody has laughed in a Broadway theater for years. All you hear is the soft, sibilant sound of creeping flesh punctuated now and then by a sharp intake of breath as somebody behind the footlights utters one of the four-letter words hitherto confined to the cozy surroundings of the lower-type barroom. (Odd to reflect, by the way, that when the word "damn" was first spoken on the New York stage—in one of Clyde Fitch's plays, if I remember rightly—there was practically a riot. Police raided the joint, and I'm not sure the military were not called out.)

Even in the musicals you never get a comedian now. The race seems to have died out, and I am convinced that the public misses them. I believe audiences want comedy, but dramatists won't let them have it. They are like stern nurses trying to make reluctant children take their spoonful of sulphur and molasses. "Why can't we have ice cream?" audiences plead, but the dramatists are firm. "Ice cream is not powerful and significant," they say. "Ice cream has no social message." Silly business all around, it seems to me, for what the nurses forget is that the kids are expected to unbelt $7.50 per spoonful and are at liberty to go and spend it elsewhere, which they do.

The process of getting back to comedy would, of course, be very gradual. At first a laugh during the progress of a play would have rather an eerie effect. People would wonder where the noise was coming from and would speculate as to whether somebody was having some sort of fit, but they would get into the way of it after a while, and it would not be so very long before it would be quite customary to audiences looking and behaving not like bereaved relatives at a wake but as if they were enjoying themselves.

Over in Europe the humorous dramatist seems, from what one can gather, to be given a squarer deal, and there is no disposition to beat him over the head with a baseball bat if he offers the clientele something lighthearted. Whether this is because the European public is less sensitive, or because they have no baseball bats, remains a moot point, but it is a fact that farces which would barely survive a single night on Broadway run for years in London, and it is pretty generally recognized that only by setting your teeth and buckling down to it with iron determination can you write anything unfunny enough to fail in Paris.

If you ask me, I think we ought to bring the population of Paris over here, teach them English, and dump them down within easy reach of Forty-fifth Street. Then we should get somewhere.

In the sixteenth century they called humor "a disorder of the blood," and though they were probably just trying to be nasty, it is not a bad description. It is, anyway, a disorder of something. To be a humorist, one must see the world out of focus. You must, in other words, be slightly cockeyed. This leads you to ridicule established institutions, and as most people want to keep faith in established institutions intact, the next thing that happens is that you get looked askance at. Statistics show that 87.03 of today's askance looks are directed at humorists, for the solid citizenry suspect them and are wondering uneasily all the time what they are going to be up to next, like babysitters with charges who are studying to be juvenile delinquents. There is an atmosphere of strain such as must have prevailed long ago when the king or prince had one of those Shakespearean fools around the castle, capering about and shaking a stick with a bladder and little bells attached to it. Tradition compelled him to employ the fellow, but nothing was going to make him like it.

"Never can understand a word that character says," he would mutter peevishly to his wife as the Fool went capering about the throne room, jingling his bells. "Why on earth do you encourage him? It was you who started him off this morning. All that nonsense about crows!"

"I only asked him how many crows can nest in a grocer's jerkin. Just making conversation."

"And what was his reply? Tinkling like a xylophone, he gave that awful cackling laugh of his and said, 'A full dozen at cockcrow, and something less under the dog star, by reason of the dew, which lies heavy on men with scurvy.' Is that a system? Was that sense?"

"It was humor."

"Who says so?"

"Shakespeare says so."

"Who's Shakespeare?"

"All right, George."

"I never heard of any Shakespeare."

"I said all right, George. Skip it."

"Well, anyway, you can tell him from now on to keep his humor to himself, and if he hits me on the head just once more with that bladder of his, he does so at his own risk. He's always hitting me on the head with his bladder. Every time he gets within arm's reach of me—socko! And for that I pay him a penny a week, not deductible. He makes me sick."

Humorists as a class are gloomy men, and it is this sense of being apart from the herd, of being, as one might say, the poison-ivy rash on the body politic, that makes them so, though they have other troubles as well. As that notable humorist E. B. White says, they are looked down on by the critics, regarded as outside the pale of literature, and seldom recognized as possessing talents worth discussing. People are very serious today, and the writer who refuses to take them seriously is viewed with concern and suspicion.

"Fiddle while Rome burns, would you?" they say to him, and treat him as an outcast.

I think we should be sorry for humorists and try to be very kind to them, for they are so vulnerable. You can blot the sunshine from their lives in an instant by telling them you don't see what there is so funny in that, and if there is something funny in it, you can take all the heart out of them by calling them facetious or describing them as "mere" humorists. A humorist who has been called mere can never be quite the same again. He frets. He re-fuses to eat his cereal. He goes about with his hands in his pockets and his lower lip jutting out, kicking stones and telling himself that the life of a humorist is something that ought not to happen to a dog, which of course in many ways is substantially true.

The most melancholy humor today is, of course, the Russian, and one can readily understand why. If you live in a country where, when winter sets in, your nose turns blue and parts from its moorings, it is difficult to be rollicking, even when primed with two or three stiff vodkas. Aleksei Kosygin probably would be con-sidered Russia's top funnyman—at least if you were domiciled in Moscow and didn't feel that way, you'd do well to keep it to your-self—and he has never got beyond the Russian proverb; and if there is anything less hilarious than a Russian proverb, we have yet to hear of it. The only way to laugh at one is to watch Kosygin and see when he does it.

"In Russia," says Kosygin, making his important speech to the Presidium, "we have a proverb—a chicken that crosses the road does so to get to the other side, but wise men dread a bandit," and then his face sort of splits in the middle and his eyes disappear into his cheeks like oysters going down for the third time in an oyster stew, and the comrades realize that this is the big boffola and that if they are a second late with the belly laugh, their next job will be running a filling station down Siberia way.

There may come a time when Russia will rise to He-and-She jokes and stories about two Irishmen who were walking up Broadway, but I doubt it. I cannot see much future for Russian humorists. They have a long way to go before they can play the Palace.

Oddly, considering that humor is so despised, people are always writing articles or delivering lectures about it, generally starting off with the words "Why do we laugh?" (One of these days some-one is going to say "Why shouldn't we?" and they won't know which way to look.) Here is what Dr. Edmund Bergler says in his book on *The Sense of Humor:*

> Laughter is a defense against a defense. Both maneuvers are instituted by the subconscious ego. The cruelty of the superego is counteracted by changing punishment into inner pleasure. The superego reproaches the ego, then institutes two new defenses, the triad of the mechanism of orality and laughter.

What do you mean, you don't know what he means? Clear as crystal. Attaboy, Edmund. Good luck to you, and don't laugh at any wooden nickels.

P. G. WODEHOUSE

THE BALLET VISITS THE
SPLENDIDE'S MAGICIAN

ﻉﻍ LUDWIG BEMELMANS

The management of the Hotel Splendide, the luxurious establishment where I once worked as a busboy, a waiter, and eventually as an assistant maître d'hôtel in the banquet department, kept on file the addresses of a number of men who were magicians, fortune-tellers, or experts with cards. One of these entertainers frequently appeared at the end of the small dinner parties which were given in the private suites of the Splendide in the boom days, before the depression put an end to such pastimes and at last brought about the demise of the Splendide itself. Our entertainers had acclimated their acts to the elegance of the hotel, and the magicians, for example, instead of conjuring a simple white rabbit from their hats, cooked therein a soufflé Alaska or brought out a prize puppy with a rhinestone collar. When young girls were present, the magician pulled from their noses and out of corsages Cartier clips, bracelets, and brooches, which were presented to them with the compliments of the host.

Among the best and most talented of our performers was Professor Maurice Gorylescu, a magician who did some palmistry on the side. He came to the hotel as often as two or three times a week. After coffee had been served, he would enter the private dining room, get people to write any number they wanted to on small bits of paper, and hold the paper to their foreheads. Then he would guess the numbers they had written down and add them up. The total would correspond to a sum he found on a dollar bill in the host's pocket. He did tricks with cards and coins, and he told people about the characteristics and the habits of dress and speech of friends long dead. He even delivered messages from them to the living.

At the end of his séances he would go into some vacant room

nearby, sink into a chair, and sit for a while with his hand over his eyes. He always looked very tired. After about half an hour he would shake himself, drink a glass of water slowly, then eat something and go home.

Professor Gorylescu earned a good deal of money. His fee for a single performance was a flat hundred dollars, and he sometimes received that much again as a tip from a grateful host. But although he worked all during the season he spent everything he made and often asked for and received his fee in advance. All he earned went to women—to the support of a Rumanian wife in Bucharest, to an American one who lived somewhere in New Jersey, and to what must have been a considerable number of New York girls of all nationalities to whom he sent little gifts and flowers.

When he came to the hotel during the day, he would hang his cane on the doorknob outside the ballroom office, ask me for a cigarette, and after a while steal a look at the book in which the reservations for small dinners were recorded. Very casually, and while talking of other things, he would turn the leaves and say something like "Looks very nice for the next two months," and put the book back. It took only a few seconds, but in this time his trick mind had stored away all the names, addresses, dates, and telephone numbers in the book. He went home with this information, called up the prospective party-givers, and offered his services.

There was a strict rule that no one should be permitted to look at these reservations, certainly not Professor Gorylescu, but I liked him, and when I was on duty in the ballroom office I would pretend not to see him when he peeked in the book. I also gave him left-over *petits fours,* candies, and after-dinner mints, of which he was very fond. He stuffed them into his pockets without bothering to wrap them up. He would wave goodbye with his immense hands, ask me to visit him soon at his home, and suggest that I bring along some *marrons glacés,* pastry, nuts—anything like that —and then he would leave, a stooping, uncouth figure, bigger than our tallest doorman.

Maurice Gorylescu lived on one of the mediocre streets that run between Riverside Drive and West End Avenue. He had a room in one of the small marble mansions that are common in that neighborhood. The rooming house in which Gorylescu lived was outstanding even among the ornate buildings of that district. It was a sort of junior Frankenstein castle, bedecked with small turrets, loggias, and balconies. It faced the sidewalk across a kind of moat—an air shaft for the basement windows—traversed by a granite bridge. The door was hung on heavy iron hinges that reached all the way across.

The character of this house was, moreover, complemented by the woman who rented its rooms, a Mrs. Houlberg. She stood guard much of the time at the window next to the moat, looking out over a sign that read "Vacancies." She always covered three-quarters of her face with her right hand, a long hand that lay diagonally across her face, the palm over her mouth, the nails of the fingers stopping under the right eye. It looked like a mask, and as if she always had a toothache.

Gorylescu lived on the top-floor front and answered to four short rings and one long one of a shrill bell that was in Mrs. Houlberg's entrance hall. Badly worn banisters led up four flights of stairs. From the balcony of his room one could see the time flash on and off in Jersey and the searchlights of a battleship in the Hudson. The room was large and newly painted in a wet, loud red, the shade of the inside of a watermelon. A spotty chartreuse velvet coverlet decorated a studio couch. Facing this was a chair, a piece of furniture such as you see in hotel lobbies or club cars, covered with striped muslin and padded with down. There was also a Sheraton highboy, which stood near a door that led into an adjoining room which was not his. From the ceiling hung a cheap bazaar lamp with carmine glass panes behind filigree panels. On shelves and on a table were the photographs of many women; in a box, tied together with ribbons in various colors, he kept packets of letters, and in a particular drawer of the highboy was a woman's garter, an old girdle, and various other disorderly trophies.

Gorylescu reclined on the studio bed most of the time when he was at home. He wore a Russian blouse that buttoned under the left ear, and he smoked through a cigarette holder a foot long. One of his eyes was smaller and lower down in his face than the other, and between them rose a retroussé nose, a trumpet of a nose, with cavernous nostrils. Frequently and with great ceremony he sounded it into an immense handkerchief. His cigar-colored skin was spotted as if with a bluish kind of buckshot, and when he was happy he hummed through his nose, mostly the melody of a song whose title was "Tu Sais."

At home he was almost constantly in the company of women. He made the acquaintance of some of them at parties where he had entertained. They brought him gifts, and if they were fat and old, he read their minds and told them things of the past and future. At other times he went looking for girls along Riverside Drive, humming through his nose, and dragging after him a heavy cane whose handle was hooked into his coat pocket.

He went to various other places to find girls. He picked them up at dance halls in Harlem, on the subway, on roller coasters. He easily became acquainted with them anywhere, and they came to his room willingly and took their chances with him. I always thought I might find one of them, dead and naked, behind the Japanese screen, where he kept a rowing machine on which he built himself up. For the space of time that I knew him, love, murder, and that man seemed to be close together and that room the inevitable theatre for it.

The Professor gave me a series of lectures during my visits to his room in which he detailed for me the routines and the mechanisms of his untidy passions. He insisted during these long *études* that the most important piece of strategy was to get the subject to remove her shoes. "Once the shoes are off, the battle is already half won," he would say. "Get a woman to walk around without shoes, without heels—she looks a fool, she feels a fool, she is a fool. Without her shoes, she is lost. Take the soft instep in your hand, caress her ankles, her calf, her knee—the rest is child's play. But remember, first off with the shoes." While he talked, he would scratch his cat, which was part Siamese. The lecture was followed by a display of the collection of photographs he himself had taken, as evidence of the soundness of his theories.

When the Russian Ballet came to town, Professor Gorylescu was not to be had for any parties at the hotel. He went to all the

performances, matinées and evenings alike, and he hummed then
the music of *"Puppenfee, L'Après-Midi d'un Faune,* and the various *divertissements,* and was completely broke. One day he was in
a state of the highest elation because he had invited a ballet
dancer to tea. He wanted me to come too because she had a
friend, who would be an extra girl for me; both of them were
exquisite creatures, he assured me, and I was to bring some tea,
marrons glacés, petits fours, and ladyfingers.

I came early and I brought everything. He darkened the room,
lit a brass samovar, laid out some cigarettes, sliced some lemons,
hid the rowing machine under the studio couch, and with the Japanese silk screen divided the room into two separate camps. On
one side was the couch, on the other the great chair. He buttoned
his Russian blouse, blew his nose frequently, and hummed as he
walked up and down. He brushed the cat and put away a Spanish
costume doll that might have made his couch crowded. He arranged the *petits fours* in saucers, and when the bell rang four
times short and one long, he put a Chopin record on his victrola.
"Remember about the shoes," he told me over his shoulder, "and
always play Chopin for ballet dancers." He quickly surveyed the
room once more, turned on the bazaar lamp, and, humming,
opened the door—and then stopped humming suddenly. He had
invited two of the dancers, but up the stairs came a bouquet of
girls, more than a dozen of them.

All at once it was the month of May in the dimmed room. The
lovely guests complimented the samovar, the cat, the music, and
the view from the balcony, to which they had opened the door,
letting much fresh air come in, which intensified the new mood.
Gorylescu's voice became metallic with introductions; he ran
downstairs to get more glasses for tea and came back breathing
heavily. All the girls, without being asked, took their shoes off
immediately, explaining that their feet hurt from dancing. They
arranged the shoes in an orderly row, as one does on entering a
Japanese house or a mosque, then sat down on the floor in a circle.
One of them even removed her stockings and put some slices of
lemon between her toes. "Ah-h-h," she said.

There started after this a bewildering and alien conversation, a
remote, foggy ritual, like a Shinto ceremonial. It consisted of the

telling of ballet stories, and seemed to me a high, wild flight into a world closed to the outsider. The stories were told over and over until every detail was correct. In all of these stories appeared Anna Pavlova, who was referred to as "Madame"—what Madame had said, what Madame had done, what she had thought, what she had worn, how she had danced. There was an atmosphere of furious backstage patriotism. The teller of each story swayed and danced with hands, shoulders, and face. Every word was illustrated; for anything mentioned—color, light, time, and person— there was a surprisingly expressive and fitting gesture. The talker was rewarded with applause, with requests for repetition of this or that part again and again, and there swept over the group of girls waves of intimate, fervent emotion.

The Professor served tea on his hands and knees and retired to the shadows of his room. He sat for a while in the great chair like a bird with a wounded wing, and then, with his sagging and cumbersome gait, he wandered around the group of innocents, who sat straight as so many candles, all with their shoes off. The room was alive with young heads and throats and flanks.

The Professor succeeded finally in putting his head into the lap of the tallest, the most racy of the nymphs. She quickly kissed him, said "Sh-h-h-h, daaaahrling," and then caressed his features, the terrible nose, the eyebrows, the corrugated temples, and the great hands, with the professional detachment of a masseuse, while she related an episode in Cairo during a performance of *Giselle* when the apparatus that carried Pavlova up out of her grave to her lover got stuck halfway, and how Madame had cursed and what she had said after the performance and to whom she had said it. An indignant fire burned in all the narrowed eyes of the disciples as she talked.

Suddenly one of them looked at her watch, remembered a rehearsal, and the girls got up and remembered us. They all had Russian names, but all of them were English, as most ballet dancers are; in their best accents, they said their adieus. With individual graces, they arranged their hair, slipped into their shoes, and thanked Maurice. Each one of them said "Daaaahrling" to us and to each other. It was Madame Pavlova's form of address and her pronunciation.

All the girls kissed us, and it was as if we all had grown up in the same garden, as if they were all our sisters. The Professor said a few mouthfuls of gallant compliments, and when they were gone he fished the rowing machine out from under the couch, without a word, and carried it in back of the Japanese screen. Together, we rearranged the room. The *marrons glacés* and the ladyfingers were all gone, but the cigarettes were still there.

LADIES' WILD

⚡ ROBERT BENCHLEY

In the exclusive set (no diphtheria cases allowed) in which I travel, I am known as a heel in the matter of parlor games. I will drink with them, wrassle with them and, now and again, leer at the ladies, but when they bring out the bundles of pencils and the pads of paper and start putting down all the things they can think of beginning with "W," or enumerating each other's bad qualities on a scale of 100 (no hard-feeling results, mind you—just life-long enmity), I tiptoe noisily out of the room and say: "The hell with you."

For this reason, I am not usually included in any little games that may be planned in advance. If they foresee an evening of "Consequences" coming over them, they whisper, "Get Benchley out of the house. Get him a horse to ride, or some beads to string —anything to get him out of the way." For, I forgot to tell you, not only am I a non-participant in parlor games, but I am a militant non-participant. I heckle from the sidelines. I throw stones and spit at the players. Hence the nickname: "Sweet Old Bob," or sometimes just the initials.

One night last summer, I detected, from the general stir among the ladies and more effete gents, that I was being eased out of the house. This meant that the gaming was about to begin. But instead of the usual clatter of pencils among the *croupiers,* I saw someone sneaking in with a tray of poker chips. They almost had me out the door when I discovered what was up.

"Well, so long, Bob," they said. "Good bowling to you."

"What's this?" I came back into the room. "Are those poker chips?"

"Sure, they're poker chips. It's all right to play poker, isn't it? The reform administration's gone out."

I assumed a hurt air. In fact, I didn't have to assume it. I was hurt.

"I don't suppose I'm good enough to play poker with you," I said. "All I'm good enough for is to furnish the liquor and the dancing girls."

"Why, we thought you didn't like games. You always act like such a goddamned heel whenever a game is suggested."

"My dear people," I said, trying to be calm, "there are games and games. 'Twenty Questions' is one game, if you will, but poker —why, poker is a man's game. It's my dish. I'm an old newspaperman, you know. Poker is the breath of life to a newspaperman." (As a matter of fact, I never played poker once when I was on a newspaper, and was never allowed to do more than kibitz at the Thanatopsis games of Broun, Adams, Kaufman, and that bunch, but poker is still my favorite game in a small way, or at least it *was.*)

Then there was a great scrambling to get me a chair, and sell me chips. "Old Bob's going to play!" was the cry. "Old Bob likes poker!" People came in from the next room to see what the commotion was, and one woman said that, if I was going to play, she had a headache. (I had ruined a game of "Who Am I?" for her once by blowing out a fuse from the coat-closet.)

As for me, I acted the part to the hilt. I took off my coat, unbuttoned my vest so that just the watch-chain connected it, lighted my pipe, and kept my hat on the back of my head.

"This is the real poker costume," I said. "The way we used to play it down on the old *Trib.* There ought to be a City News ticker over in the corner to make it seem like home."

"I'm afraid he's going to be too good for us," said one of the more timid ladies. "We play for very small stakes, you know."

"The money doesn't matter," I laughed. "It's the game. And anyway," I added modestly, "I haven't played for a long time. You'll probably take me good." (I wish now that I had made book on that prediction.)

It was to be Dealer's Choice, which should have given me a tip-off right there, with three women at the table, one the dealer.

"This," she announced, looking up into space as if for inspiration, "is going to be 'Hay Fever.' "

"I beg pardon," I said, leaning forward.

" 'Hay Fever,' " explained one of the men. "The girls like it. One card up, two down, the last two up. One-eyed Jacks, sevens, and nines wild. High-low."

"I thought this was going to be poker," I said.

"From then on you play it just like regular poker," said the dealer.

From then on! My God! Just like regular poker!

Having established myself as an old poker-fan, I didn't want to break down and cry at the very start, so I played the hand through. I say I "played" it. I sat looking at my cards, peeking now and then just to throw a bluff that I knew what I was doing. One-eyed Jacks, sevens, and nines wild, I kept saying that to myself, and puffing very hard at my pipe. After a minute of owlish deliberation, I folded.

The next hand was to be "Whistle Up Your Windpipe," another one which the girls had introduced into the group and which the men, weak-kneed sissies that they were, had allowed to become regulation. This was seven-card stud, first and last cards up, deuces, treys, and red-haired Queens wild, high-low-and-medium. I figured out that I had a very nice straight, bet it as I would have bet a straight in the old days, and was beaten to eleven dollars and sixty cents by a royal straight flush. Amid general laughter, I was told that an ordinary straight in these games is worth no more than a pair of sixes in regular poker. A royal straight flush usually wins. Well, it usually won in the old days, too.

By the time the deal came to me, my pipe had gone out and I had taken my hat off. Between clenched teeth I announced: "And this, my frands, is going to be something *you* may not have heard of. This is going to be *old-fashioned draw-poker,* with *nothing* wild." The women had to have it explained to them, and remarked that they didn't see much fun in that. However, the hand was played. Nobody had anything (in comparison to what they had been having in the boom days), and nobody bet. The hand was over in a minute and a half, amid terrific silence.

That was the chief horror of this epidemic of "Whistle Up Your Windpipe," "Beezy-Weezy," and "Mice Afloat." It made old-fashioned stud seem tame, even to me. Every time it came to me, I elected the old game, just out of spite, but nobody's heart was in it. I became the spoil-sport of the party again, and once or twice I caught them trying to slip the deal past me, as if by mistake. Even a round of jack-pots netted nothing in the way of excitement, and even when I won one on a full-house, there was no savor to the victory, as I had to explain to the women what a full-house was. They thought that I was making up my own rules. Nothing as small as a full-house had ever been seen in that game.

The Big Newspaper Man was taken for exactly sixty-one dollars and eight cents when the game broke up at four A.M. Two of the women were the big winners. They had finally got it down to a game where everything was wild but the black nines, and everyone was trying for "low."

From now on I not only walk out on "Twenty Questions" and "Who Am I?" but, when there are ladies present (God *bless* them!), I walk out on poker. And a fine state of affairs it is when an old newspaperman has to walk out on poker!

SHAGGY-DOG STORIES

ᵛᔡ BENNETT CERF

Shaggy-dog stories, as almost everybody must know by this time, are the kind of tales in which animals talk, humans do inexplicable things, and the punch lines make no sense at all. They are generally anathema to literal-minded females. There is nothing like a string of shaggy-dog stories to make your wife's Aunt Minnie cut short a visit and go back where she came from. They receive their name from the following legend.

A Kansas City barfly picked up a year-old copy of the London *Times* one day—don't ask me how it got there—and found therein a personal ad offering a ten-pound reward for the return of a very shaggy dog to its bereft owner in Bishop's Bowes, Essex. Ten minutes later he stumbled over the shaggiest darn pup you ever saw. Being a man of decision, he promptly bundled the canine under his arm, took the Twentieth Century to New York, the *Queen Mary* to Southampton, and a limousine to Bishop's Bowes. In keen anticipation, he sought out the lady who had advertised, and rang her bell. She answered herself. "You lost a shaggy dog, madam," he reminded her, holding up the pooch. "Would this be it?" "Good heavens, no," she snapped. "It wasn't *that* shaggy"— and slammed the door in his face.

Well, now that we've settled that, we propose to give you thirty-two examples of the species. We figure that fewer than that would not do the subject full justice; more might set the most avid addicts to baying at the moon. Note that we have numbered the entries. You can't tell the bayers without a number.

1. Two race horses fretted impatiently in adjoining stalls the night before a Kentucky Derby. "You might as well save yourself the effort of competing tomorrow," spoke one, "I've got the Derby sewed up." "Says you," scoffed the other. "What makes you so sure

of yourself?" "Didn't you see my owner whispering in my ear just now?" said the first horse. "He was telling me that if I won tomorrow, he'd give me two extra bales of hay. And, brother, that ain't money!"

2. "A quarter's worth of rat poison," ordered the man at the delicatessen store. "Yes, sir," the clerk answered. "Shall I wrap it up for you?" "Oh, you needn't bother," the man said pleasantly. "I'll eat it here."

3. A bat family was flying home from a picnic—Papa Bat, Mama Bat, and Sonny Bat. "Thank heaven that picnic's over," said Sonny Bat. "Now the four of us can have some peace." "Four?" queried Papa. "I only see three." Sonny Bat flared up. "You know very well I can't count," he grumbled.

4. "This dog," Mr. Weber once said to Mr. Fields, "is worth five hundred dollars." To which Mr. Fields replied, "How could a dog save that much money?"

5. A customer entered a saloon and ordered a dozen martinis. He poured the liquor onto the floor, and began munching contentedly on the glasses themselves. The stems, however, he would have no traffic with. A barfly watched the performance with absorbed interest, but pointed to the twelve stems. "You darn fool," he said. "You're leaving the best part."

6. The oysters found a fine new bed several miles up the Sound, and were happily packing their belongings—all except little Mary Oyster, who sat sobbing bitterly in a corner. "What's the matter?" asked her father anxiously. "We'll have a wonderful new home. There's nothing to cry about." "Oh, yes, there is," wailed Mary. "Johnny Bass will never be able to find me now, and I love him with all my heart." "But does Johnny Bass reciprocate your devotion?" inquired the parent. "Indeed he does," Mary assured him. "Last night he took me in his arms at the end of the pier out there. First he kissed me here on the forehead. Then he kissed me here on the lips. And then—my God, my *pearl!*"

7. A very shy young man sat next to a glamorous debutante at a dinner party. In the middle of the main course he seized a bowl of

succotash and poured it over the debutante's chic coiffure. The young lady rose indignantly. "How dare you?" she blazed, plucking corn and peas out of her hair. "How dare you throw succotash at me?" The young man blanched. "Good heavens," he stammered. "Was that succotash? I thought it was spinach!"

8. A man's ear was bleeding like a stuck pig. "I bit myself," he explained. "That's impossible," said the doctor. "How can a man bite himself in the ear?" The man said, "I was standing on a chair."

9. Two herrings stopped at a neighborhood café for a couple of snifters. One of them disappeared for a moment, and a puzzled onlooker accosted the one who was left alone at the bar. "Where is your brother?" he challenged. "How in heck should I know," replied the indignant herring. "Am I my brother's kipper?"

10. A man staggered from a railroad car, his complexion a sickly green. "Riding backwards for six hours," he explained. "I never *could* stand that." "Why," his wife inquired, "didn't you ask the party sitting opposite to change seats with you?" "I couldn't do that," said the man. "There wasn't anybody there."

11. A crotchety old bachelor saw a gaily plumed parrot go under the hammer at a country auction, and suddenly decided that the bird might be good company for him on lonely evenings. The bidding grew unexpectedly stiff, but the bachelor was carried away by the spirit of the occasion and before he quite realized what he had done, he bought the Poll for forty-nine dollars. He carried it home, and stood it on the table before him. "Now," he commanded, "talk to me!" The parrot simply drew in its head and glared at him. "I said talk to me," repeated the man. "After all, I bought you to keep me company." Again the parrot glared but said nothing. "Good heavens," cried the exasperated gentleman. "Do you mean to say that after what I paid for you, you can't even *talk?*" "Can't even talk?" echoed the parrot. "Who in hell do you think it was that bid you up to forty-nine dollars?"

12. A cotton-tail rabbit, nibbling thoughtfully at his evening carrot, noticed that his son was in a particularly jovial mood. "What

makes Junior so happy?" he asked. Mamma rabbit explained, "He had a wonderful time in school today. He learned how to multiply."

13. At a gala ship concert aboard a liner, a trained parrot did his act, and then teetered excitedly on his perch in the wings while an extraordinary magician performed feats of legerdemain. First he made a goldfish disappear, then a buxom blonde assistant, finally a chest containing three husky sailors. At that moment the liner was struck by a torpedo. The parrot found himself all alone on the Atlantic Ocean, bobbing up and down on a piece of driftwood, with nothing else in sight. "Amazing," marveled the Poll. "What will he think of next?"

14. (Very, very old.) "Give me a soda," commanded the young sprout, "without flavor." "Without what flavor?" asked the soda jerk. "Without vanilla." "Ain't got no vanilla." "All right, gimme one without strawberry."

15. Two brothers, identical twins, often went fishing together. One twin was always lucky. The other could never catch a thing. They could stand right next to each other and one brother would haul in fish after fish while the other's line dangled idly in the water. One day the unlucky twin decided on a desperate course. He woke in the middle of the night and put on his brother's clothes. He took his brother's rod and went to the very spot where his brother had caught thirty-four trout the day before. For three hours he stood there without getting a nibble. Finally his hopes rose when he saw a magnificent trout swimming his way. The fish ignored the bait and, leaping out of the water, called, "Hey, bud, where's your brother?"

16. Sitting opposite Miss Haas on a northbound subway train one evening sat a man calmly reading his paper with three pigeons resting on top of him—one on his head, the others on his shoulders. Miss Haas contemplated the situation until she could stand it no longer. She tapped his paper, and said, "Pardon me, but what on earth are you doing with those pigeons in the subway?" "Them?" said the man. "I really don't know, lady. They musta got on at 59th Street."

17. A man dropped in to pay a friend an unexpected visit, and was amazed to find him playing chess with his dog. The man watched in silence for a few minutes, then burst out with "That's the most incredible dog I ever saw in my life!" "Oh, he isn't so smart," was the answer. "I've beaten him three games out of four!"

18. One day a man said to Billy Rose, "Would you like to see me dive into a barrel of water from a thousand feet?" Billy Rose said he certainly would, and next day he called his workmen and had them set up a thousand-foot ladder. Mr. Rose held his breath while the man climbed to the top, and stared fascinated as he took a flying leap and landed, splash, in the barrel of water.

"Magnificent," said Billy Rose. "I'll hire you for $100 a week."

"No," said the man.

"$250 a week," said Billy Rose.

"No," said the man.

"You drive a hard bargain," said Billy Rose, "but your act is worth it. Let's not count pennies. I'll hire you for a thousand a week."

"No," said the man.

"Say, fellow," said Billy Rose, "how much do you want to jump into that barrel?"

"Nothing," said the man. "This is the first time I ever did it, and I don't like it."

19. A worm met another worm coming up from the ground and declared, "You're very beautiful and I'd like to marry you." "Don't be a dope," was the reply. "I'm your other end."

20. (One of the very first.) An elephant looked down at a mouse and exclaimed, "You're about the puniest, most insignificant object I ever laid eyes on." "I'm not always this little," the mouse squeaked angrily. "I've been sick."

21. A dignified old clergyman owned a parrot of which he was exceedingly fond, but the bird had picked up an appalling vocabulary of cuss words from a previous owner and, after a series of embarrassing episodes, the clergyman decided he would have to kill his pet. A lady in his parish suggested a last-ditch remedy. "I have a female parrot," she said, "who is an absolute saint. She sits

quietly on her perch and does nothing but pray from morning until night. Why don't you bring your parrot over and see if my own bird's good influence doesn't reform him?" The clergyman said it was worth a trial, and the next night arrived with his pet tucked under his arm. The bird took one look at the lady parrot and chirped, "Hi, toots. How about a little loving?" "Come to mama," cried the lady parrot gleefully. "What do you think I've been praying for all these years?"

22. A doctor saved a baby elephant's life in the jungle, then returned to America. Years later he was down on his luck, and had to borrow a quarter to see the circus when it came to town. Out came the elephants. One of them saw the doctor, and trumpeted recognition. He wrapped his trunk around the doctor, lifted him out of the twenty-five-cent seat—and planked him down in a box seat worth three dollars.

23. A kangaroo yanked her young one out of her pouch and gave it a healthy smack on the backside. "I'll teach you," she declared, "to eat crackers in bed!"

24. When the manager of the Brooklyn ball club lost his star center fielder on the eve of a crucial swing through the West, he sent out a frantic call for a replacement. Almost a week went by and there were no applications. The manager sat dejectedly on the bench with his head in his hands. He heard an apologetic whinny behind him, and looking around, saw a horse standing there.

"Go away," he said to the horse. "Can't you see I've got a headache?"

"But I'm applying for that spot in center field," said the horse.

"That's ridiculous," snapped the manager. "Horses don't play baseball—not even in Brooklyn!"

The horse insisted, however, and finally the manager allowed him to exhibit his wares. It developed that he could field like Tris Speaker and hit like Joe Di Maggio. The delighted manager promptly inserted him into the lineup.

In the ninth inning of that day's game, with the score 0-0, the horse strode to the plate and lashed a wicked liner against the right-field fence.

Then—to everyone's amazement—he stood stock still at the plate, twirling his bat.

"Run, you idiot, run!"—beseeched the frantic manager. "This means the game!"

"Don't be silly," said the horse. "Who ever heard of a horse running bases?"

25. A colony of ostriches—ninety-nine birds in all—had their heads buried neatly in the sand when ostrich number one hundred came galumping onto the scene. He looked about in a puzzled way and inquired, "Where on earth *is* everybody?"

26. A reporter was assigned, a long time ago, to interview Mr. Barnum's favorite midget, Tom Thumb. The hotel clerk directed the reporter to Room 308, but when he knocked on that door, it was opened by a giant fully nine feet tall. "I must have the wrong room," apologized the newsman. "Who were you looking for?" countered the giant. "Tom Thumb, the dwarf," laughed the reporter. "Well, come in," said the giant. "I'm Tom Thumb." "You Tom Thumb!" the reporter scoffed. "Why, you're nine feet tall!" "I know," said the giant. "But, you see, this is my day off."

27. Mr. Nussbaum was a regular patron of Finkelstein's Shangri-La Bar and Grille. One evening he declared, "I feel like some fried flounder tonight." The waiter brought a generous portion, but just as Nussbaum was about to dive in, the flounder shook his head and threw a warning glance. Nussbaum ran for the sidewalk. A month later he tried again. "We got fresh flounder for you," said the waiter. "Just came in today." But at the last moment it turned out to be the same old flounder, who shook his head even more vigorously than the first time. "This does it," cried Nussbaum. "Never do I come to this joint again!" Some weeks later his wife took him to a swanky Park Avenue hotel. "Here I will get flounder what is flounder," exulted Nussbaum. The waiter brought a steaming platter, beautifully garnished with parsley and lemon. Just as Nussbaum was reaching for his fork the flounder lifted his head from the plate. "Ah ha!" he sneered. "So Finkelstein's ain't good enough for you no more!"

28. "Do you realize," said a man in a cafeteria to a stranger across the table, "that you are reading your newspaper upside down?"

"Of course I realize it," snapped the stranger. "Do you think it's easy?"

29. A pigeon came home very late for dinner one evening, with his feathers bedraggled, and his eyes bloodshot. "I was out minding my own business," he explained, "when bingo! I get caught in a badminton game!"

30. The bartender noticed that his customer had a big carrot behind his ear, but he decided not to mention it. "Probably just waiting for people to ask him what it's for. I'll fool him." For twenty-seven consecutive days the customer appeared, with a carrot always tucked behind his ear. Then, on the twenty-eighth day, the routine was varied: a banana had replaced the carrot! The bartender could stand it no longer. "What's the idea of that banana behind your ear, fellah?" he demanded, leaning over the counter. "Couldn't find no carrot today," explained the customer.

31. A couple of frogs were dining at the Ritz one evening. "You're angry at me," accused Abdul Amnal (he was a Turkish frog). "You haven't spoken to me all evening." "It isn't that at all," explained the other with some difficulty. "I just can't talk tonight. I've got a man in my throat."

32. A brown horse, hitched to a milk wagon, looked up one morning to see a poster staring her in the face. The Ringling Circus was in town! She calmly trotted over to the stage door of Madison Square Garden, and entered. "Hi, girls!" she neighed, to be greeted with noisy expressions of surprise and delight. "But, Beulah," protested one nag, "what are you doing with that cheesy milk wagon you're hitched to? A year ago you were the star of the show here, with blue plumes over your ears, and beautiful performers somersaulting on your back!" "Aw," answered Beulah, "what can you expect from that darn Hollywood agent of mine?"

AN APE ABOUT THE HOUSE

ARTHUR C. CLARKE

Granny thought it a perfectly horrible idea; but then, she could remember the days when there were *human* servants.

"If you imagine," she snorted, "that I'll share the house with a monkey, you're very much mistaken."

"Don't be so old-fashioned," I answered. "Anyway, Dorcas isn't a monkey."

"Then what is she—it?"

I flipped through the pages of the Biological Engineering Corporation's guide. "Listen to this, Gran," I said. " 'The Superchimp (Registered Trade-mark) *Pan Sapiens* is an intelligent anthropoid, derived by selective breeding and genetic modification from basic chimpanzee stock—' "

"Just what I said! A monkey!"

" '—and with a large-enough vocabulary to understand simple orders. It can be trained to perform all types of domestic work or routine manual labor and is docile, affectionate, housebroken, and particularly good with children—' "

"Children! Would you trust Johnnie and Susan with a—a *gorilla?*"

I put the handbook down with a sigh.

"You've got a point there. Dorcas *is* expensive, and if I find the little monsters knocking her about—"

At this moment, fortunately, the door buzzer sounded. "Sign, please," said the delivery man. I signed, and Dorcas entered our lives.

"Hello, Dorcas," I said. "I hope you'll be happy here."

Her big, mournful eyes peered out at me from beneath their heavy ridges. I'd met much uglier humans, though she was rather an odd shape, being only about four feet tall and very nearly as wide. In her neat, plain uniform she looked just like a maid from one of those early twentieth-century movies; her feet, however, were bare and covered an astonishing amount of floor space.

"Morning, Ma'am," she answered, in slurred but perfectly intelligible accents.

"She can speak!" squawked Granny.

"Of course," I answered. "She can pronounce over fifty words, and can understand two hundred. She'll learn more as she grows used to us, but for the moment we must stick to the vocabulary on pages forty-two and forty-three of the handbook." I passed the instruction manual to Granny; for once, she couldn't find even a single word to express *her* feelings.

Dorcas settled down very quickly. Her basic training—Class A Domestic, plus Nursery Duties—had been excellent, and by the end of the first month there were very few jobs around the house that she couldn't do, from laying the table to changing the children's clothes. At first she had an annoying habit of picking up things with her feet; it seemed as natural to her as using her hands, and it took a long time to break her of it. One of Granny's cigarette butts finally did the trick.

She was good-natured, conscientious, and didn't answer back. Of course, she was not terribly bright, and some jobs had to be explained to her at great length before she got the point. It took several weeks before I discovered her limitations and allowed for them; at first it was quite hard to remember that she was not exactly human, and that it was no good engaging her in the sort of conversations we women occupy ourselves with when we get together. Or not many of them; she did have an interest in clothes, and was fascinated by colors. If I'd let her dress the way she wanted, she'd have looked like a refugee from Mardi Gras.

The children, I was relieved to find, adored her. I know what people say about Johnnie and Sue, and admit that it contains some truth. It's so hard to bring up children when their father's away most of the time, and to make matters worse, Granny spoils them when I'm not looking. So indeed does Eric, whenever his ship's on Earth, and I'm left to cope with the resulting tantrums.

Never marry a spaceman if you can possibly avoid it; the pay may be good, but the glamour soon wears off.

By the time Eric got back from the Venus run, with three weeks' accumulated leave, our new maid had settled down as one of the family. Eric took her in his stride; after all, he'd met much odder creatures on the planets. He grumbled about the expense, of course, but I pointed out that now that so much of the housework was taken off my hands, we'd be able to spend more time together and do some of the visiting that had proved impossible in the past. I looked forward to having a little social life again, now that Dorcas could take care of the children.

For there was plenty of social life at Port Goddard, even though we were stuck in the middle of the Pacific. (Ever since what happened to Miami, of course, all major launching sites have been a long, long way from civilization.) There was a constant flow of distinguished visitors and travelers from all parts of the Earth— not to mention remoter points.

Every community has its arbiter of fashion and culture, its *grande dame* who is resented yet copied by all her unsuccessful rivals. At Port Goddard it was Christine Swanson; her husband was Commodore of the Space Service, and she never let us forget it. Whenever a liner touched down, she would invite all the officers on Base to a reception at her stylishly antique nineteenth-century mansion. It was advisable to go, unless you had a very good excuse, even though that meant looking at Christine's paintings. She fancied herself as an artist, and the walls were hung with multicolored daubs. Thinking of polite remarks to make about them was one of the major hazards of Christine's parties; another was her meter-long cigarette holder.

There was a new batch of paintings since Eric had been away: Christine had entered her "square" period. "You see, my dears," she explained to us, "the old-fashioned oblong pictures are terribly dated—they just don't go with the Space Age. There's no such thing as up or down, horizontal or vertical out *there*, so no really modern picture should have one side longer than another. And ideally, it should look *exactly* the same whichever way you hang it—I'm working on that right now."

"That seems very logical," said Eric tactfully. (After all, the Commodore was his boss.) But when our hostess was out of ear-shot, he added, "I don't know if Christine's pictures are hung the right way up, but I'm sure they're hung the wrong side to the wall."

I agreed; before I got married I spent several years at the art school and considered I knew something about the subject. Given as much cheek as Christine, I could have made quite a hit with my own canvases, which were now gathering dust in the garage.

"You know, Eric," I said a little cattily, "I could teach Dorcas to paint better than this."

He laughed and answered, "It might be fun to try it some day, if Christine gets out of hand." Then I forgot all about the matter —until a month later, when Eric was back in space.

The exact cause of the fight isn't important; it arose over a community development scheme on which Christine and I took opposing viewpoints. She won, as usual, and I left the meeting breathing fire and brimstone. When I got home, the first thing I saw was Dorcas, looking at the colored pictures in one of the weeklies—and I remembered Eric's words.

I put down my handbag, took off my hat, and said firmly: "Dorcas—come out to the garage."

It took some time to dig out my oils and easel from under the pile of discarded toys, old Christmas decorations, skin-diving gear, empty packing cases, and broken tools (it seemed that Eric never had time to tidy up before he shot off into space again). There were several unfinished canvases buried among the debris, which would do for a start. I set up a landscape which had got as far as one skinny tree, and said: "Now, Dorcas—I'm going to teach you to paint."

My plan was simple and not altogether honest. Although apes had, of course, splashed paint on canvas often enough in the past, none of them had created a genuine, properly composed work of art. I was sure that Dorcas couldn't, either, but no one need know that mine was the guiding hand. She could get all the credit.

I was not actually going to lie to anyone, however. Though I would create the design, mix the pigments, and do most of the execution, I would let Dorcas tackle just as much of the work as she could handle. I hoped that she could fill in the areas of solid color, and perhaps develop a characteristic style of brushwork in the process. With any luck, I estimated, she might be able to do perhaps a quarter of the actual work. Then I could claim it was all hers with a reasonably clear conscience—for hadn't Michelangelo and Leonardo signed paintings that were largely done by their assistants? I'd be Dorcas' "assistant."

I must confess that I was a little disappointed. Though Dorcas quickly got the general idea, and soon understood the use of brush and palette, her execution was very clumsy. She seemed unable to make up her mind which hand to use, but kept transferring the brush from one to the other. In the end I had to do almost all the work, and she merely contributed a few dabs of paint.

Still, I could hardly expect her to become a master in a couple of lessons, and it was really of no importance. If Dorcas was an artistic flop, I would just have to stretch the truth a little farther when I claimed that it was all her own work.

I was in no hurry; this was not the sort of thing that could be rushed. At the end of a couple of months, the School of Dorcas had produced a dozen paintings, all of them on carefully chosen themes that would be familiar to a Superchimp at Port Goddard. There was a study of the lagoon, a view of our house, an impression of a night launching (all glare and explosions of light), a fishing scene, a palm grove—clichés, of course, but anything else would rouse suspicion. Before she came to us, I don't suppose Dorcas had seen much of the world outside the labs where she had been reared and trained.

The best of these paintings (and some of them *were* good— after all, I should know) I hung around the house in places where my friends could hardly fail to notice them. Everything worked perfectly; admiring queries were followed by astonished cries of "You don't say!" when I modestly disclaimed responsibility. There was some skepticism, but I soon demolished that by letting a few privileged friends see Dorcas at work. I chose the viewers for their ignorance of art and the picture was an abstraction in red, gold, and black which no one dared to criticize. By this time, Dorcas could fake it quite well, like a movie actor pretending to play a musical instrument.

Just to spread the news around, I gave away some of the best paintings, pretending that I considered them no more than amusing novelties—yet at the same time giving just the barest hint of jealousy. "I've hired Dorcas," I said testily, "to work for me—not for the Museum of Modern Art." And I was *very* careful not to draw any comparisons between her paintings and those of Christine: our mutual friends could be relied upon to do that.

When Christine came to see me, ostensibly to discuss our quarrel "like two sensible people," I knew that she was on the run. So I capitulated gracefully as we took tea in the drawing room, beneath one of Dorcas' most impressive productions. (Full moon rising over the lagoon—very cold, blue, and mysterious. I was really quite proud of it.) There was not a word about the picture, or about Dorcas; but Christine's eyes told me all I wanted to know. The next week, an exhibition she had been planning was quietly canceled.

Gamblers say that you should quit when you're ahead of the game. If I had stopped to think, I should have known that Christine would not let the matter rest there. Sooner or later, she was bound to counterattack.

She chose her time well, waiting until the kids were at school, Granny was away visiting, and I was at the shopping center on the other side of the island. Probably she phoned first to check that no one was at home—no one human that is. We had told Dorcas not to answer calls; though she'd done so in the early days, it had not been a success. A Superchimp on the phone sounds exactly like a drunk, and this can lead to all sorts of complications.

I can reconstruct the whole sequence of events. Christine must have driven up to the house, expressed acute disappointment at my absence, and invited herself in. She would have wasted no time in getting to work on Dorcas, but luckily I'd taken the precaution of briefing my anthropoid colleague. "Dorcas make," I'd said, over and over again, each time one of our productions was finished. "Not Missy make—*Dorcas* make." And, in the end, I'm sure she believed this herself.

If my brainwashing, and the limitations of a fifty-word vocabulary, baffled Christine, she did not stay baffled for long. She was a lady of direct action, and Dorcas was a docile and obedient soul.

Christine, determined to expose fraud and collusion, must have been gratified by the promptness with which she was led into the garage studio; she must also have been just a little surprised.

I arrived home about half an hour later, and knew that there was trouble afoot as soon as I saw Christine's car parked at the curb. I could only hope I was in time, but as soon as I stepped into the uncannily silent house, I realized that it was too late. *Something* had happened; Christine would surely be talking, even if she had only an ape as audience. To her, any silence was as great a challenge as a blank canvas; it had to be filled with the sound of her own voice.

The house was utterly still; there was no sign of life. With a sense of mounting apprehension, I toptoed through the drawing room, the dining room, the kitchen, and out into the back. The garage door was open, and I peered cautiously through.

It was a bitter moment of truth. Finally freed from my influence, Dorcas had at last developed a style of her own. She was swiftly and confidently painting—but not in the way *I* had so carefully taught her. And as for her subject . . .

I was deeply hurt when I saw the caricature that was giving Christine such obvious enjoyment. After all that I had done for Dorcas, this seemed sheer ingratitude. Of course, I know now that no malice was involved, and that she was merely expressing herself. The psychologists, and the critics who wrote those absurd program notes for her exhibition at the Guggenheim, say that her portraits cast a vivid light on man-animal relationships, and allow us to look for the first time at the human race from outside. But I did not see it *that* way when I ordered Dorcas back into the kitchen.

For the subject was not the only thing that upset me: what really rankled was the thought of all the time I had wasted improving her technique—and her manners. She was ignoring everything I had ever told her, as she sat in front of the easel with her arms folded motionless on her chest.

Even then, at the very beginning of her career as an independent artist, it was painfully obvious that Dorcas had more talent in either of her swiftly moving feet than I had in both my hands.

CONFESSIONS OF A GALLOMANIAC

✑ FRANK MOORE COLBY

Down to the outbreak of the war I had no more desire to converse with a Frenchman in his own language than with a modern Greek. I thought I understood French well enough for my own purposes, because I had read it off and on for twenty years, but when the war aroused sympathies and sharpened curiosities that I had not felt before, I realized the width of the chasm that cut me off from what I wished to feel. Nor could it be bridged by any of the academic, natural, or commercial methods that I knew of. They were either too slow or they led in directions that I did not wish to go. I tried a phonograph, and after many bouts with it I acquired part of a sermon by Bossuet and real fluency in discussing a quinsy sore throat with a Paris physician, in case I ever went there and had one. I then took fourteen conversation lessons from a Mme. Carnet, and being rather well on in years at the start, I should, if I had kept on diligently, have been able at the age of eighty-five to inquire faultlessly my way to the post office. I could already ask for butter and sing a song written by Henry IV— when my teacher went to France to take care of her half-brother's children. I will say this for Mme. Carnet. I came to understand perfectly the French for all her personal and family affairs. No human being has ever confided in me so abundantly as she did. No human being has ever so sternly repressed any answering confidences of my own. Her method of instruction, if it was one, was that of jealous, relentless, unbridled soliloquy.

Thrown on the world with no power of sustaining a conversation on any other subject than the members of the Carnet family, I nevertheless resolved to take no more lessons but to hunt down French people and make them talk. What I really needed was a governess to take me to and from my office and into the park at

32

noon, but at my age that was out of the question. Then began a career of hypocritical benevolence. I scraped acquaintance with every Frenchman whom I heard talking English very badly, and I became immensely interested in his welfare. I formed the habit of introducing visiting Frenchmen to French-speaking Americans, and sitting, with open mouth, in the flow of their conversation. Then I fell in with M. Bernou, the commissioner who was over here buying guns, and whose English and my French were so much alike that we agreed to interchange them. We met daily for two weeks and walked for an hour in the park, each tearing at the other's language. Our conversations, as I look back on them, must have run about *like this:*

"It calls to walk," said he, smiling brilliantly.
"It is good morning," said I, "better than I had extended."
"I was at you yestairday ze morning, but I deed not find."
"I was obliged to leap early," said I, "and I was busy standing up straight all around the forenoon."
"The book I prayed you send, he came, and I thank, but positively are you not deranged?"
"Don't talk," said I. "Never talk again. It was really nothing anywhere. I had been very happy, I reassure."
"Pardon, I glide, I glode. There was the hide of a banane. Did I crash you?"
"I noticed no insults," I replied. "You merely gnawed my arm."
Gestures and smiles of perfect understanding.

I do not know whether Bernou, who like myself was middle-aged, felt as I did on these occasions, but by the suppression of every thought that I could not express in my childish vocabulary, I came to feel exactly like a child. They said I ought to think in French and I tried to do so, but thinking in French when there is so little French to think with, divests the mind of its acquisitions of forty years. Experience slips away for there are not words enough to lay hold of it. Knowledge of good and evil does not exist; the sins have no names; and the mind under its linguistic limitations is like a rather defective toy Noah's ark. From the point of view of Bernou's and my vocabulary, Central Park was as the Garden of Eden after six months—new and unnamed things everywhere. A dog, a tree, a statue taxed all our powers of description, and on a complex matter like a policeman our minds could not meet at all. We could only totter together a few steps in any mental direction. Yet there was a real pleasure in this earnest interchange of insipidities and they were highly valued on each side. For my part I shall always like Bernou, and feel toward him as my childhood's friend. I wonder if he noticed that I was an old, battered man bothered with a tiresome profession. I certainly never suspected that he was. His language utterly failed to give me that impression.

After I lost Bernou I fastened upon an unfrocked priest who had come over here and gone into the shoe trade—a small, foxy man, who regarded me, I think, in the light of an aggressor. He wanted to become completely American and forget France, and as I was trying to reverse the process, I rather got in his way. He could talk of medieval liturgies and his present occupation, but nothing in between, and as he spoke English very well, his practical mind revolted at the use of a medium of communication in which one of us almost strangled when there was another available in which we were both at ease. I could not pump much French out of him. He would burst into English rather resentfully. Then I took to the streets at lunch-time and tried newsdealers, book-shops, restaurants, invented imaginary errands, bought things that I did not want, and exchanged them for objects even less desirable. That kept a little conversation going day by day, but on the whole it was a dry season. It is a strange thing. There are more than thirty thousand of them in the city of New York, and I had always heard that the French are a clannish folk and hate to learn another language, but most of my overtures in French brought only English upon me. The more pains I took the more desirable it seemed to them that I should be spared the trouble of continuing. I was always diving into French and they were always pulling me out again. They thought they were humane.

French people hate broken French worse than most of us hate broken English. But when dragged out into the light of English I tried to talk just as foolishly in order that they might think it was not really my French that was the matter with me. Sometimes that worked quite well. Finding me just as idiotic in my own language they went back to theirs. It certainly worked well with my friend M. Bartet, a paralytic tobacconist in the West Thirties near the river, to whom my relation was for several months that of a grandchild, though, I believe, we were of the same age. He tried to form my character by bringing me up on such praise-worthy episodes of his early life as he thought I was able to grasp.

Now at the end of a long year of these persistent puerilities I am able to report two definite results: In the first place a sense of my incapacity and ignorance infinitely vaster than when I began, and in the second a profound distrust, possibly vindictive in its origin, of all Americans in the city of New York who profess an acquaintance with French culture, including teachers, critics, theater audiences, lecture audiences, and patronesses of visiting Frenchmen.

It was perhaps true, as people said at the time, that a certain French theatrical experiment in New York could not continue for the simple reason that it was too good a thing for the theater-going public to support. It may be that the precise equivalent of the enterprise, even if not hampered by a foreign language, could not have permanently endured. Yet from what I saw of its audiences, critics, enthusiasts, and from what I know of the American Gallophile generally, including myself, I believe the linguistic obstacle to have been more serious than they would have us suppose —serious enough to account for the situation without dragging in our aesthetic incapacity. It was certainly an obstacle that less than one-half of any audience ever succeeded in surmounting. I do not mean that the rest of the audience got nothing out of it, for so expressive were the players by other means than words, that they often sketched the play out in pantomime. The physical activities of the troupe did not arise, as some of the critics declared, from the vivacity of the Gallic temperament; nor were they assumed, as others believed, because in the sevententh century French actors had been acrobats. These somewhat exaggerated gestures were occasioned by the perception that the majority of the spectators were beginners in French. They were supplied by these ever-tactful people as a running translation for a large body of self-improving Americans.

I do not blame other Americans for dabbling in French, since I myself am the worst of dabblers, but I see no reason why any of us should pretend that it is anything more than dabbling. The usual way of reading French does not lead even to an acquaintance with French literature. Everybody knows that words in a living language in order to be understood have to be lived with. They are not felt as a part of living literature when you see them pressed out and labeled in a glossary, but only when you hear them fly about. A word is not a definite thing susceptible of dictionary explanation. It is a cluster of associations, reminiscent of the sort of men that used it, suggestive of social class, occupation, mood, dignity or the lack of it, primness, violences, pedantries, or platitudes. It hardly seems necessary to say that words in a living literature ought to ring in the ear with the sounds that really belong to them, or that poetry without an echo cannot be felt.

It may be that there is no way out of it. Perhaps it is inevitable that the colleges which had so long taught the dead languages as if they were buried should now teach the living ones as if they were dead. But there is no need of pretending that this formal acquaintance with books results in an appreciation of literature. No sense of the intimate quality of a writer can be founded on a verbal vacuum. His plots, his place in literature, his central motives, and the opinions of his critics could all be just as adequately conveyed if his books were studied in the language of the deaf and dumb. Of course, one may be drawn to an author by that process but it would hardly be the artistic attraction of literature; it is as if one felt drawn to a woman by an interest exclusively in her bones.

Elementary as these remarks may seem I offer them to Gallophiles without apology. On the contrary I rather fear that I am writing over their heads.

DOUBLE THAT ORDER!

✒ PARKE CUMMINGS

The other day I went into a local general store and stated: "I want six nail files."

The clerk looked at me curiously for a minute, and finally said: "Of course, it's none of my business, but why do you want so many?"

Drawing myself up to my full height, and looking him squarely in the chest, I replied, with quiet dignity: "To clean my nails with."

Again he regarded me with curiosity. "I assumed that," he admitted, "but why six?"

"I will explain," I said patiently. "When I take the six files home, my son, John, will immediately grab one of them, attempt to wedge loose a stuck part of his electric train with it, and break off the tip. He will then take a second file, use it more carefully, but mislay it. My young daughter will employ a third one to loosen a tough knot in her shoelaces. It will never be seen again. My wife, seeing three remaining files on my bureau, will assume I have more than I need, and appropriate one of them to make up for the one she left in the washroom of the Hotel Ardmont. The disappearance of the fifth file will never be explained. If I have good luck, this will still leave me a file with which—as I have previously stated—to clean my nails."

The clerk nodded understandingly. "It's pencils that go in our house," he said.

"In ours too," I said. What I was outlining to this fellow was the Theory of Protective Mass Purchasing, one to which I have long subscribed. This, of course, should not be confused with any system of quantity buying where the object is to get a cheaper unit price—as when you buy five bushels of grapefruit, half of which

37

spoil. I paid the straight retail price for my half dozen files, and my saving was not a financial one.

My objective was purely one of availability. The law of averages operates inexorably with nail files—and other articles I shall mention—but, by buying in quantity, you at least give it a temporary knockout. You get it down on the floor and under control, overwhelmed by sheer force of numbers. It will, of course, eventually get up off the floor to plague you again, but that fleeting respite is all I ask for.

Drinking tumblers should be similarly mass purchased, but on a far more generous basis. To buy six tumblers for a family of four is the height of futility. Before the first meal, one will be spirited to the bathroom for a toothbrush container, a second will get broken, and a third will be appropriated by one of the younger children for mixing water colors—which means that, at dinner, some member of the family will have to use an old jelly glass or go thirsty. A dozen is the minimum plausible purchase, but two dozen is the figure I hold out for. And the number should go up in geometrical, not arithmetical, proportion. For instance, for a family of eight, you should buy eight dozen glasses, not four.

Anybody who allows himself to get down to one door key should, of course, be held for observation. Some member of the family will develop the theory that this article is the solution to a locked trunk in the attic. It will be lugged up there, mixed in with a quantity of other unidentifiable keys, and then either lost or thrown away in disgust when it doesn't work. This means that you will have to hire a locksmith, at a fancy price, to make an impression of your door lock, and furnish you with new keys. On the other hand, it is a relatively inexpensive matter to have any hardware store turn out duplicate keys for you *provided* you have one suitable to serve as a model. My personal feeling is that no family should have less than eight keys per door, at least three of which should be cached in the safe-deposit box.

Here are some further recommendations the next time you go to the store. (I am assuming a family of four–six. Up this accordingly if yours is larger.)

Hammers: Six. (Small children, you have noted, eat hammers.)

Hair combs: Three per person. People are constantly lugging combs out of the house and losing them. Certain types of combs simply evaporate in unfavorable weather.

Paring knives: Use your judgment here, but reflect that in a typical family a paring knife will be used for: cutting string; whittling a closet door that sticks; mumblety-peg; severing heavy wire; cutting flowers; repairing light sockets; sharpening pencils; opening packages; paring fingernails; cleaning corroded water pipes; prying off bottle tops; trimming loose branches off small trees and shrubs; miscellaneous repairs to sporting equipment, such as baseball bats, tennis rackets, skis, sleds, air rifles; and (occasionally) paring vegetables. From this you should be able to estimate the chances of a housewife finding one in her kitchen drawer, and in good repair, when she wants to use it.

Adhesive substances (Scotch tape, court plaster, tire tape, etc.): If my recommendations go into effect, these will hereafter be sold in quarter-mile, half-mile, and mile units.

Paper: To draw on, I mean. A small home-type paper mill installed just off the garage may keep you abreast of the demand, though I doubt it. A gesture in this direction will be appreciated at the office in any case.

Radio sets: Two per room per child, with a spare gross in the basement—and two tickets, for you, to Atlantic City.

Mittens: Just take all they have in Susie's size. If other customers have to go without, that's their hard luck.

FATHER HAS TROUBLE WITH THE LAND OF EGYPT

⊷§ CLARENCE DAY

One winter when most of us boys were away, Mother was invited to go to Egypt with Mrs. Tytus and two or three others. Mrs. Tytus's son, Bob, was in charge of the party. They were going to sail up the Nile in a houseboat, they would see Luxor and Memphis, and altogether it seemed to be an ideal opportunity. Mother loved travel. She was eager to see any place that was new to her, even a place that was comparatively near-by like the Whitneys' camp up in Maine, and as Egypt was ten times as far away it seemed ten times as attractive.

She explained to Father what a wonderful chance it was. He was not impressed. He said she wanted to go anywhere, always, and he had never seen such a woman. Most women were glad to have a home, he said, and knew enough to appreciate it, but the only thing Mother seemed to want was to be on the go.

He went on to say that he himself had some sense, however, and that he would no more think of going to Egypt than to the North Pole. In a year or two, if he could get away from business, they might go to London and Paris once more, but not one of the Day family had ever set foot in Egypt and nobody else he knew had, either, except Charlie Bond, who was one of those restless fellows anyhow and was always doing queer things. He said it was a wild and entirely unsuitable country, and that never in any circumstances whatever would he take Mother to Egypt.

"But that's just why I want to go, Clare, dear. You don't understand."

Father stared at her, and said, "What! What's why you want to go? Of course I don't understand."

"Why, because you don't like it. I thought it would please you."

The veins in Father's forehead began to swell. "You thought it would *please me?*"

"Oh Clare, dear, don't be stupid. I knew you wouldn't want to take me over to Egypt yourself, but don't you see, if Mrs. Tytus takes me, you won't ever have to."

This theory that Mother was only trying to save him trouble by getting on a ship and going to Egypt completely dumbfounded Father. But Mother clung firmly to it. She said of course she hated to have him miss seeing the Pyramids, but still she wouldn't enjoy dragging him off there if he was so unwilling, so he could just stay home and be comfortable in his own way while she went quietly over with Mrs. Tytus and hurried straight back.

To help clinch the matter, she brought Mrs. Tytus to see him. She brought young Bob Tytus, too. She told Father how much her letter of credit should be, and when he protested, she said she was saving him money, because it would be nearly twice as much if he took her himself.

When Father said violently that he wished her to remain at his side, she said everybody had to go away sometimes, and Dr. Markoe had warned her she must.

Dr. Markoe was a man Father liked. Mrs. Tytus was tactful and beautiful. Mother was pertinacious. Between them all, they actually bore Father down, and on the appointed day Mother got aboard the ship, letter of credit and all, with Father swearing that now he would have to worry about her all winter, and he wouldn't be happy for a minute until she got back.

"Goodbye, darling," she said. "Do be quiet and nice while I'm gone."

"I won't!" he shouted, kissing her, and he marched stiffly off, saying, "I hope you are satisfied," and then turned back at the foot of the gangplank, calling loudly, "Dear Vinnie!" Mother waved her hand, the whistles blew hoarsely, and the crowds swirled and jostled, hiding these two from each other as the ship slid away.

Father began looking for letters the very next morning, and when none came he cursed the pilot and the postman, and said that he had a bad headache. But a letter did arrive in a few days, when the pilot had had time to mail it, and after the first three or four weeks we heard from Mother often.

Some of the letters told us how she was constantly meeting people she knew, not only on the ship but at every port where Mrs. Tytus and she went ashore. "Your mother has the damnedest number of friends I ever heard of," said Father. "She's everlastingly meeting some old friend or other wherever she goes. I never see people I know when I'm traveling. But there isn't a city in Europe where your mother wouldn't spot a friend in five minutes." And when a letter came saying she had just climbed Mt. Vesuvius and had found old Mr. and Mrs. Quintard of Rye at the top, peering down into the crater, Father said that upon his soul he never knew anyone like her.

Other letters were full of household advice and instructions about menus, or warnings to Father to keep an eye on the rubber tree and to speak about washing the curtains. Others abused the bad habits of foreigners and the inconveniences and troubles she met. "Well, why doesn't she stay home, then?" Father demanded triumphantly. Though he swore at every foreigner who dared to inconvenience her, he relished the complaints in these letters.

But when Mother left civilization behind her, even a far outpost like Cairo, and went off up the Nile in a thing called a dahabeah, manned by native boatmen, and when letters came from queer-sounding ancient cities in the interior, Father got nervous. He said it was a wild, harum-scarum thing to do. Moreover, it was entirely needless. He said he could see all of Egypt he wanted to without leaving New York—there were enough musty old mummies in the Museum to satisfy anybody. "But your mother wouldn't look at them; no, they weren't dead enough for her; she had to go traipsing off to see a mummy on its native heath. Why, somebody even brought an obelisk over here at great expense," he went on, "and left it to crumble away in the Park, where people can see it for nothing, but for some reason or other it isn't crumbly enough for your mother."

There were letters about the strange range of hills back of Thebes, and the great colonnades at Karnak, and the statues and tombs, which Father pished at impatiently; and there were letters about fleas, and moonlight and Nubian songs, and finally letters with snapshots. Father said he hated these photographs. He spent a great deal of time staring at them in deep disapproval. There was one in particular of Mother looking very roguish and chic in her voluminous dress, sitting way up on top of a tall and insolent camel, with two big black men in white turbans standing off at one side. No other member of the party around. Not a soul in sight but the black men and Mother. Father looked at that photograph often and groaned about it at night, and kept shouting things to himself about "the ends of the earth."

Soon after that, Mother turned around and headed for home. Father grew more and more eager to have her back, every day. Up to this time he had been comparatively quiet, for him, but the nearer the day of her return came the more noisy and impatient he got. Even at the pier, he made indignant remarks about how slow the ship was getting in.

He forgot this mood, however, the minute he hugged her, and he instantly took charge of her things—all except her black bag, which she would never let anyone touch—and he ordered all the customs inspectors around and got Mother through in a jiffy, and he found a man to shoulder her trunk and he picked out the best hackman, and as the carriage rattled off over the cobblestones, Mother said she was glad to be back.

Father had taken particular pains to have everything in the house in its place, so that when Mother came in the door, she would say that home was just the way she had left it. Instead, what she actually said was "Oh, this poor room! Why, I never!" and she put down the black bag and began setting the chairs at different angles and moving her favorite ornaments affectionately as she straightened them out. "Poor things," she said, as she patted them, "didn't anybody know enough to turn you around the way you belong?" Father followed her, looking puzzled at these minute changes, and calling her attention to the rubber tree, which had grown half a foot. "Well," Mother said, "of all the forlorn objects, with those dead leaves left hanging there!" But when Father's face fell and she saw how disappointed he looked, she smiled at him to console him and said, "You did the best you could, darling." And she climbed upstairs to unpack.

The letter of credit had been very much on Father's mind. He had never before given Mother the management of any such sum. He was so happy to have her back that he said nothing about this at first. He was waiting for Mother to speak of it. But she said nothing either.

He had two expectations about it, and he didn't know which to trust. One was hopeful but slightly unreal. The other, based on long experience, was pessimistic.

It had been a large letter of credit, not as much as Mrs. Tytus had recommended but still, he felt, generous. He felt he had a right to expect that Mother hadn't spent all of it, but had left a substantial balance undrawn which he could now restore to his bank account. His other and realer expectation was that she had spent every cent and had possibly even had to borrow from Mrs. Tytus besides. The fact that she was avoiding the subject pointed to this latter outcome.

One night, after she had gone up to bed, she came back down for a moment to hand him some papers. "You might be going over these, Clare," she said. "I couldn't keep track of everything for you; I tried my best but I couldn't. But I saved all the bills." And she went off to bed again.

Father checked them over, one by one, carefully. They were full of strange-looking details:

Cairo, FEB. 24, 1900.

MRS. DAY,
Room 195,
Shepheard's Hotel.

To 1 Passage to Second Cataract	£ 23. 0.0.
To 60 days on Dahabeah Tih	£ 85.16.0.
	£ 108.16.0.

"Second Cataract!" Father muttered to himself vehemently. What would such a woman do next?

These bills supplied Father with more details than he had hoped to keep track of, and there was none of them that he felt much inclined to dispute. But as there were still several hundred dollars unaccounted for, he waited for Mother to confess what she had done with the balance.

Day after day went by without her saying one word. He began to fear that things must be serious. He became so alarmed that it would have been a relief to him to know the worst and be done with it. But do what he could—without direct questioning—he could get nothing out of her.

Mother had noticed his fumbling hints of course, and she did have a confession to make. But first she went and had a long talk with a young girl she was fond of—a girl whose name was Wilhelmine Johnson, whom George afterward married. Mother confided to Wilhelmine in secret that the situation was this: she hadn't spent all her letter of credit but she hated to give up the balance. It was wicked of her to feel that way, she supposed, but she meant to keep it herself.

Wilhelmine instantly took a strong stand about this. She said that on no account should Mother hand over that money to Father. Mother had always wanted to have some money of her own, Wilhelmine reminded her, and now here was her chance.

As Mother listened to this advice she felt happy, but she also felt frightened. It seemed to her far more daring to hang onto that money than it had been to ride on a camel. But while she was away all those months she had had a taste of what independence was like, and she was reluctant to drop back into her Victorian role.

When at last she nerved herself to tell Father, he felt better at once, but he smilingly reproved her for not having come to him sooner; and as to her keeping the money he said that that was all nonsense. He said that she was home now, thank God, and as he always paid all her bills at home she had no use for this money.

"Yes I have too," Mother said.

"Well, what will you use it for, then?" Father asked.

Mother didn't wish to explain. As a matter of fact she had no very definite ideas as to what she wanted some cash of her own for—she only knew that she wanted it. She said, "Oh, there are lots of little things I could use it for, Clare. Things I'd like to get when I need them, without so much talk."

This seemed unconvincing to Father. He demanded the balance. He felt that he was the natural custodian of any such fund and the only safe place for it was in his bank account, as Mother, of course, didn't have one. But Mother insisted on hiding it away in her own bureau drawer. Father pointed out how reckless this was, but he could do nothing with her. That voyage to Egypt had changed her; she was always much harder to manage after that sail up the Nile.

As a gracious concession, however, she presented Father with a large pale blue scarab, mounted to use as a scarfpin, which she said she hadn't really meant to let him have until Christmas. Father looked at this object without enthusiasm and asked what it was. When he was told that it was the image of a sacred beetle, he immediately pushed it away. He didn't want any dead beetles in his scarf, he declared. He told Mother she could send it right back to the tomb it had come from. He said that he begged to inform her that he was not a mummy.

THE INDOMITABLE DUCK

ﻬ CHARLES G. FINNEY

Mrs. Farrier had been by turns amused, amazed, and exasperated by the interests which successively held her sons' attention, but the discoveries at Frogpond gave a new direction to her thoughts. The more she reflected on them the more she decided she was greatly distressed by their frank enthusiasm for the high mysteries of amphibian sex life and reproduction. She felt it was not right for two such small boys to have witnessed so much and to be able to recount it with such accuracy and delight. She doubted if she was bringing them up properly.

So, not knowing quite what else to do, she took the matter up with the Reverend Mr. Jackson, pastor of Grace Episcopal Church. She wound up by saying, "And that's all they talk about any more, Mister Jackson. It's just awful. I don't know what to think. Isn't there something I can do about it?"

Mr. Jackson pulled at his lip. "There is," he said, "nothing essentially wrong in their knowing such things. Of course, it is a pity they are not somewhat older. I believe the best thing to do is to distract their attention from the frogs and center it on something else. Boys never concentrate on things very long. Find something else to interest them, Misses Farrier."

"But bugs and frogs and things for pets are all that does interest them!" wailed Mrs. Farrier.

"Very well! Get them some other pet! Some less . . . uh . . . exotic pet, if that's the word I want. Get them a chicken, Misses Farrier!"

"A chicken?"

"Yes. Certainly. They evidence interest in pets, you say. Very well! Get them a pet that is domesticated—something which will be profitable for them to study and care for. In that way, you mold and shape your sons' natural inclinations. They have this zest for observing animal life. Very well! Put it to use, Misses Farrier."

"Well, I don't know," she said doubtfully. "I just can't picture them somehow, getting very excited about a chicken . . . but I'll try."

She called her boys to her next morning. "If," she said, "you will both promise me faithfully to take good care of them, I will get you some chickens, and you may have them for pets. They're far more interesting than frogs, and, if they lay any eggs, we can have them for breakfast."

No immediate enthusiasm was discernible on her sons' countenances. In fact, Willie said, "Aw, heck, mamma, chickens are so *dumb*. Ever'body, pretty near, has got chickens."

"They're not dumb at all," said Mrs. Farrier firmly. She knew if the boys ever started arguing it would mean the end of the chicken project. "You've never had any chickens, so you don't know a single thing about them. As a matter of fact, chickens are very interesting. You can even train them to do little tricks. When I was a girl I had a bantam rooster that would ride around on my shoulder. I know you'll both love chickens after you have them a while."

"Yeh, but, look, mamma, we like wild stuff that we got to catch. Don't we, Tom? Like those frogs at Frogpond."

"Uh huh," said Tom. "Chickens ain't no fun at all. They're dumb. Ever'body's got 'em."

"Nevertheless," said Mrs. Farrier in desperation, "I think it would be good for you to have some chickens. If, after a month or so, you decide you don't like them, you can get rid of them. But I'm going to insist that you give them a fair trial."

She called the community market where the local farmers sold their wares through a sort of brokerage system. The clerk there, who knew her, told her she could get young live pullets for fifty cents apiece.

"Now, Willie," she said, "here's a dollar and a half. You and Tom go to the market and buy three pullets. The clerk knows you're coming, and he'll see that you get nice ones. He'll put them in a box for you, and you bring them home. You can keep them in the woodshed till you build them a regular coop."

The boys went to market, but went reluctantly. "Doggone," they kept wondering to each other, "whur did mamma ever get the idear we wanted any old fool chickens?"

The market, a hollow square with pens all around, aroused their interest slightly. Its acrid poultry smell piqued their nostrils, and the cries of the fowls piqued their ears. They wandered round and round, talking and looking.

Just at the end of their tour of inspection, they saw the muscovy drake. After seeing him that once, they looked at nothing else.

He was a huge snow-white brute of a duck with wattles that were blood red and a thin, cruelly hooked yellow beak. His short tail feathers curled into tight knots; his gnarled webbed feet were broader than the boys' outspread hands. He was arrogant and rude and in a vile temper, and he flew at them whenever they came too close to his bars. They looked at him and fell in love with him, for he was no ordinary barnyard fowl. He was something heraldic, as strange as a wild bird from a wild, far-off island. They looked at him and decided they must have him.

They went straightway to the clerk.

"We're Misses Farrier's kids," Willie told him, "and we come to get that big white duck down there . . . if he ain't too expensive."

"Now, wait a minute," said the clerk. "I thought yer mother said you was to git some chickens. I know cockeyed well she did."

"Naw," said Willie. "Mamma said we could get chickens if we didn't find nothing else that suited us better. But we think now we'll take that duck."

"Well, I think now I'd better phone yer old lady and make sure," said the clerk.

"It won't do no good," said Willie. "She went downtown and won't be back for a long time."

"Well . . . look here: are you kids lying to me?"

"No, sir. If mamma'd seen the duck 'fore she called yuh, she'd a'said for you to sell it to us 'stead of any old fool chickens."

"Well . . . all right. It's not my funeral. Come on and git it. It's two bucks."

Both boys said simultaneously, "Good gosh!"

"Now what's the matter?" demanded the clerk.

"We ain't got that much money."

"How much have you got?"

"Dollar and a half."

"Well, that's just too tough, boys. The duck's two bucks. Old man Renfro brought it in from the farm and put the price on it himself."

The boys were very near to tears. "Wouldn't Mister Renfro sell it just a little cheaper?" Tom finally asked.

"I dunno. Whyn't yuh ask him? There he is over there—the big guy in the straw hat. It's his duck."

They went dubiously to Mr. Renfro.

"Mister Renfro . . ."

"That's me, gentlemen."

"Uh . . . we wanta buy yer duck."

"My duck? Here, now, you ought to break these things to a fellah more gentle-like. Which duck? I've got better'n three hundred."

"We mean the big white one in the coop over there," said Willie timidly.

"Oh! Well, now, that can be arranged real simple-like. Two bucks, an' the bird's yers forever."

"But we ain't got but a dollar and a half," explained Tom.

"No sale," said Mr. Renfro.

"Aw, gosh, couldn't you please just sell him to us a little bit cheaper?"

Mr. Renfro looked at the boys carefully for the first time. They were twitching with nervousness, and their eyes were full of tears.

"Hey, wait a minute!" he protested. "Don't make yerselves sick over it, fer gosh sakes. What do you kids want with a fool duck, anyhow?"

"We want him for a pet," sobbed Tom. "But we ain't got but a dollar and a half."

"Here, here!" said Mr. Renfro. "Take it easy, boy. Take it easy. Who are you kids? What's yer names?"

"We're Misses Farrier's boys," said Willie.

"Do you know 'em?" Mr. Renfro asked the clerk.

"I know their mother," said the clerk. "They're all right, I guess."

"Well, leave 'em have the damn duck, then," said Mr. Renfro. "I never did see kids act such a way before. Lord!"

"You mean we can have it for a dollar and a half?" asked Willie.

"Yep. Take it and get out of here."

"Oh, gee! Thanks! Gosh, that's nice of yuh! C'mon, Tom!"

"Wait! Wait!" said the clerk. "How you going to get him home?"

"Aw, we can carry him," said Willie. "Under our arms."

"Aw, no, you can't," said Mr. Renfro. "That drake's a regular man-killer. Get a gunny sack and pack him home in that. If he starts to act rambunctious, slap him up agin a telephone pole, and that'll tone him down."

The clerk found a burlap bag and attempted to sack up the fowl.

At once a magnificent battle took place. The drake used wings and claws and beak; the clerk fished about feebly with one hand. When the battle was over the drake still huffed and snorted in the coop, the clerk was blown and perspiring, and his hand and forearm were lacerated and scratched.

"That thing sure 'nough is a man-killer," he acknowledged to Mr. Renfro.

Mr. Renfro had watched the battle with a great deal of interest.

"I'll git the so-and-so out there for you," he said determinedly. "You mustn't fool around the way you do. After all, that ain't no weak-kneed chicken in there. That's a real bird. Hold the sack wide open, boys; I aim to git some action."

Mr. Renfro shoved his big brawny arm into the pen, and, after long preliminary maneuvers, got the drake by the neck and choked it down.

"Look out! Yer gonna kill it!" screamed Willie.

"Shut up!" grunted Mr. Renfro. "Who's catching this duck? Git ready with that bag like I tole yuh."

He yanked the drake out in a rumpled mass and thrust it deep into the burlap sack. He twisted a length of baling wire about the sack's mouth, sealing it tight.

"There! That's the way to handle 'em! Now, take the fool thing and git out of here."

Willie picked up the sack at one end and Tom picked up the other. They left the market in jubilation. The drake squawked and thrashed about and made rousing trouble in the sack, but the boys never released their grips till they got him home.

Tom said, "We better get him in the woodshed 'fore we let him out."

Willie said, "Yeh, and we better close the door good, too."

Their mother was on the back porch as they came into the yard. She called to them brightly, "Did you get nice chickens, boys?"

They looked at each other in alarm; they had forgotten her completely.

Willie said in a low voice, "Better go ahead and tell her and get it over with." And in a loud and studiedly casual voice he said, "Mamma, the chickens they had there weren't no good, so we got us a duck instead."

"A duck? Willie, I told you plainly to get chickens!"

"But, mamma, the chickens wasn't any good."

"Now, Willie, why can't you ever do as you're told?"

"Aw, mamma, they ain't really much difference between chickens and ducks, 'cept that ducks are lots better. Gee, we got a swell duck, mamma!"

"Let me see it," said Mrs. Farrier.

"Well, you'll hafta look at him in the woodshed, mamma, for

he's kinda wild. It'll be a couple of days 'fore we get him tamed good."

"For heaven's sake, what kind of duck is it?"

"It's a big white one," said Tom.

Mrs. Farrier went with her sons to the woodshed. There, they entered, closed the door carefully, and let their prize out of the sack. The prize appraised his new surroundings and masters with loud, exasperated hisses. He took immediate command of the interior of the woodshed. First, he stalked about haughtily, flapping his wings and nibbling at his back feathers. Then he made a quick rush at Tom and drove him into a corner. He made a similar rush at Mrs. Farrier and drove her to the door. He hissed warningly at Willie, plainly indicating to him to keep his distance.

"Now, what in the world," said Mrs. Farrier in distress, "will you ever be able to do with the horrible thing? He won't ever get tame or gentle. I never saw such ferocity in all my life."

"Aw, mamma," Willie assured her, "if we just let him alone for a while till he sorta gets used to the place, he'll be all right. I think he'll get real tame, mamma."

"Well, you watch him while I get out of here. I might have known something like this would happen. I send you down to get three nice little chickens, and you come back with this atrocious goose, or whatever it is. Really, Willie, I don't know what to think of you sometimes. I'm awfully provoked."

"Yeh, but, heck, mamma, he can't hurt nothing in the shed."

"Well, mind you keep him here, then. You remember that, too, Tom; don't ever let him out of here."

"Aw, we'll take good care of him, mamma. Gee, I guess we ought to feed him. What does he eat, mamma?"

"Raw meat, from the looks of him," said Mrs. Farrier. "But, come on in, and I'll give you some bread crusts. He might like them. He ought to have a pan of water, too."

They fed their great drake and watered him, and, after subsequent experimental feedings, they found he would eat anything and everything in the way of fish, flesh, fowl, fruit, root, or leafy vegetable or insect. He had an overwhelming, outrageous appetite, and his table manners were terrible. He would rush upon the boys when they came bearing him foodstuffs, knock the pan from their hands, batter them away with his thrashing wings, and gobble up ravenously every speck of what they brought him. Then he would strut about and hiss at them, dash his head into his pan of water, throwing drops and rivulets over his back and tail, and, done with that rite, he would march up and face them and make loud, guttural noises in demand of more food.

On the whole, however, the drake's career in the woodshed was harmless and fairly peaceable. It was when the boys prevailed upon their mother to let them take him out for an airing that travail began in the neighborhood.

They said one day, "Heck, mamma, he's getting so tame now that he'll eat out of his pan real gentle-like without first trying to knock it outta your hand like he used to all the time. Why can't we just tie a cord to his leg and take him out so's he can walk around a little? He's probably awful tired of being cooped up in the woodshed all the time."

"No," said Mrs. Farrier. "I still don't trust him."

"But, mamma, there can't possibly nothing happen. We'll tie a good, strong cord to his leg, and we'll watch him real close."

"No."

"Aw, mamma, please!"

"Well . . . but just for a little while."

So they secured a long piece of jute wrapping twine and went to give their drake an airing.

A wild ten-minute free-for-all took place before they overpowered him and hobbled him with the string. Shaken and definitely uncertain, they were nevertheless determined to go through with the project; they opened the door and ushered him out.

The drake strode out scolding and gabbling, turning now and then to hiss violently at them without the faintest trace of conciliation or gratitude in his tone. He proved exceptionally intractable on his leash, and they discovered almost at once that the sole way to make any progress was to follow along behind him wherever he wanted to go and not attempt to guide him themselves.

He toured the back yard haphazardly, muttering discontentedly to himself, and snarling at them whenever the cord impeded his newest whim. He pulled up flowers abandonedly, shaking them about in his beak and spitting them out without eating them. He came upon the washtub half full of water, jumped in with a great delighted splash, and gave himself such a hectic bath that when he was through the boys were as wet as he was from his splashings.

"Maybe we better put him back now," said Tom, who was becoming weary of the strain.

"Yeh, I guess we better," agreed Willie. "He's had a good bath and a lotta exercise."

But there was no agreement at all on the part of the drake. At the first tug on the cord, he went into a frenzy. He tried to snatch himself free of them but succeeded only in ignominiously tripping himself when the cord jerked his foot from under him. That brought his rage to the explosion point. He swooped at Willie and buffeted him with his wing knobs. He gave a lunge at Tom, while Willie yanked desperately at the cord.

Then the cord snapped off at the drake's ankle, and the big white bird was free.

"Golly, he's got loose!" gasped Willie. He jumped for him and made a futile flying tackle.

It was futile because the drake uncovered a brand-new accomplishment; at least, it was brand new to the harassed Farriers. He ran a short distance along the ground, spread his wings, flapped mightily, and soared ponderously into the air to light on the roof of the woodshed. There, contemptuously, he looked down at them. Beneath him, all around, were the other back yards of the neighborhood. He surveyed them in triumph. He gave vent to a bugling scream of victory.

"Gosh, how we ever gonna get him back?" despaired Tom.

"I dunno," said Willie. "Maybe we can't."

He was right; they couldn't. The drake looked down at them once more, then catapulted himself from the woodshed roof and went flapping off. They didn't see him again for some time, but they heard plenty about him.

Mrs. Farrier, when her sons tearfully told her of their prize's escape, was sincerely and deeply relieved; she even counseled them not to search for him too hard. "He'll get run over, or a dog will kill him, or something. It really isn't much use looking for him," she said.

Tom and Willie did not, at first, look very much, for they didn't know just where to look. They thought that perhaps the drake had flown off to the wilds somewhere and was living as drakes normally should live—amid ponds and mud banks and water-waving greenery. Only a few days were necessary, however, to demonstrate that actually the fowl had remained in the immediate neighborhood and therein had uncovered new deviltries unsuspected even by his former masters.

The first news they heard about him after his escape was brought by Joseph L. (Tar) Beach, who lived a block down the street from the Farriers'. Tar Beach was a carpenter who sold and installed tarpaper roofs. He was a thin, constantly embittered person; the only pleasure of his life was his chickens: he had a back yard full of fine plymouth rocks which were the feathered apples of his acrimonious eye.

Tar's news about the drake was bad.

He came to the Farrier house the fourth day after the drake had left, and he pounded loudly on the Farrier back door.

"Why, hello, Mister Beach," said Mrs. Farrier. "How are you this morning?"

"Well, I'm a-doing all right, thank ye, but, now, lissen here. Miz Farrier, ain't them kids of your'n got 'em a big ole white duck?"

"Well . . . uh . . . they did have, but it got away a few days ago and we haven't seen it since."

"Uh huh? Yeh. That's what I figgered. That's jest zackly what I figgered. Now, lissen here, Miz Farrier, that there doggone duck got in among my plymouth rocks right early this morning an' he jest raised ole tunket. Yer a lady, Miz Farrier, an' I cain't tell yuh jest what it was he did, but I am a-tellin yuh this: you better keep that critter away from my plymouth rocks er there'll be hell tuh pay."

"Oh, dear!" said Mrs. Farrier. "Did he hurt your chickens?"

"Well, he like tuh kilt three uh the roosters, m'am, but that ain't nothing at all compared with what he done to my hens. Why, I never seen sech a thing in all my life! A doggone duck actin' that-away with hens! That there duck ain't nacheral, Miz Farrier. Why . . . why, it's a devil—that's what it is, a doggone devil."

"I wish," said Mrs. Farrier, "you would have killed it. I wouldn't have objected in the least."

"Kilt it? Why, doggonit, Miz Farrier, what d'yuh figger I tried tuh do? I went after it with a club the first time, but the doggone thing flew up on the barn and scritched at me. So then I went an' got my ole double-bar'l. But I didn't have nothin' but quail loads, an' they didn't faze him a bit. Anyhow, that duck ain't nacheral, an' you better do something about him. He's your'n, ain't he?"

"But what can I do, Mister Beach?"

"I dunno," said Tar Beach. "But you gotta do something. I cain't have that thing a-botherin' my hens no more like he done. I still dunno what's gonna come of it."

"Well . . . I'll try, Mister Beach. And I'm really awfully sorry that it happened."

"Yer sorry? Well, so'm I sorry. I kin sure tell yuh that!" And Tar Beach went broodingly home, unhappy, uncertain, and indignant over what had befallen his flock.

The drake, in addition to his other unpleasant characteristics, was a fearful and perverted lecher. Tar Beach's placid plymouth rocks had caught the drake's wicked eye that morning, doubtless as he was winging down the alley back of Tar's chicken yard.

He swooped around short and lighted right among them with a loud, lewd gabble. Tar's roosters rushed to the protection of their harem, but there was nothing on earth the mighty muscovy welcomed more than a rough-and-tumble brawl with a choice pullet as the guerdon for the victor. The roosters were already handicapped, for Tar had clipped their spurs to neutralize any fights they might have among themselves; they were virtually helpless against the rage of the drake. He attacked them almost before they showed indication of attacking him; he weighed as much as all three of them together; and his beak and wing knobs did fearful damage.

Once they lay gasping in corners, he turned his attention to the hens. It was while he was vigorously disporting himself among them that Tar came out to see what the excitement was about.

Ordinarily no more profane than the average man, Tar, at the sight of the drake and what he was doing, strained his vocabulary to the point where it was reduced to mere gibberish. He seized a mop handle and made for the white demon. The muscovy saw Tar coming, read his intent, whirled about, and launched himself at Tar's head. Tar's experience with poultry had never encompassed fighting with a horn-mad duck; he retreated without honor. When he reappeared on his back-porch stoop, armed with his fowling piece and yelling imprecations, he could not loose a volley, for the drake had shielded himself with hens. And, when the drake did eventually fly to the barn peak, Tar's ill-aimed broadside was ineffective; the light birdshot bounced off the duck as if they were raindrops.

Mrs. Farrier told her boys a censored version of what Tar had told her and sent them out to look for the muscovy. "The moment I set eyes on that duck I knew he was going to make trouble," she said. "Oh, if you'd only gotten chickens as I told you!"

"Yeh, but the doggone thing musta gone crazy," said Willie. "Shoot, I don't see why a duck should wanta fight chickens. I thought they got along swell."

Tom said, "Maybe he's like a eagle or something. They all-a time attack chickens, don't they, mamma?"

"Yes," said Mrs. Farrier, "but not the way your duck does."

Willie and Tom took broom handles and went off on what was the first of many duck hunts. But they failed to locate the big drake; and the score stood one up for the muscovy and one down for the neighborhood.

Mrs. George Multin, Sr., lived several houses farther down the street from Tar Beach. She was pretty much against pets in general and on principle ("They are such fearful nuisances, my dear!"), and she restricted her son George, Jr., to one rabbit. It was a big fluffy white rabbit named Lulu; it had pink ears and the gentlest of mien. Mrs. Multin had personally selected the rabbit for her son, and she felt toward it a certain tolerance. In fact, whenever Mrs. Multin thought of Lulu it was with definite amiability. For Lulu didn't bark, as would a dog; Lulu didn't have kittens all the time, as would a cat; Lulu didn't require a lot of care, as would a canary; and Lulu wasn't delicate, as is a goldfish.

"Furthermore," Mrs. Multin would say, "Lulu isn't outlandish like those horrible things the Farrier boys are always catching and bringing home. I really enjoy George Junior's having Lulu. It's educational for boys to have pets."

Mrs. Multin, too, was pretty much against the Farrier boys in general and on principle. "I don't see how a nice woman like Helen Farrier could have had such brats, and if I've told George Junior once I've told him a million times that I'll tan the hide off him if I ever catch him playing with them!"

Lulu had a little hutch where she stayed most of the time but sometimes in the cool of the morning George, Jr., would put Lulu in the side yard, which was fenced in, and let her hop around and nibble at grass.

And, so, one day when Lulu had been put in the side yard and was hopping about nibbling at grass, Mrs. Multin went to the window and looked out to see if Lulu were all right before she, Mrs. Multin, went to the grocery store.

She looked out the window, and the pleasant smile on her face switched to an expression of frigid horror. For a great white bird with blood-red wattles clustered about its eyes and beak was chasing Lulu round and round the fenced side yard. It hissed as undoubtedly hisses a demon; its wings were half-spread like a demon's; its predatory beak was open, avid to seize Lulu.

Lulu doubled and redoubled with astonishing agility, but the great white bird was as relentless as death is supposed to be. It never ceased pursuit for a second; finally, it made a quick turn on its awkward webbed feet, got hold of Lulu by one large pink ear and, at the same time, folded her under its immense wing.

Lulu gave a shrill squeak; there followed a scene which gave Mrs. Multin nightmares for a long while afterward. It was atrocious and outrageous and unbelievable. It was fantastic and downright insane. It was incredible that such a thing could happen on a sunny summer morning in the Multins' fenced side yard. And the most hideous thing about it all was that Lulu seemed to enjoy it. It was as if Lulu were, indeed, another Leda. . . .

"Lulu! Lulu!" screamed Mrs. Multin. "Stop that! Get away from that awful thing! Oh, Lulu . . . how could you . . . oh, dear!"

She felt that she ought to interfere, but she didn't quite know how to go about it. She remained inside and had a case of nerves until George, Jr., came home.

"Go out right away and look at Lulu," she ordered. "It was the most ghastly thing! I'm afraid to step foot out of the house."

"What was it happened, Mother?" asked her bewildered son.

"A big white bird attacked Lulu. It was awful, I tell you. Go see if she's all right."

Lulu seemed to be, as far as George, Jr.'s, cursory examination could indicate. "What was it happened to her, Mother?" he pressed. "I cain't see nothing wrong."

"Well, I still can't believe it, George Junior. But I looked out the window, and there was a horrible goose or something chasing her about. I thought surely it would . . . uh . . . kill her."

"Was it a big ole white duck?" asked George, Jr.

"Oh, heavens, it was far too large for a duck!"

"I betcha," said George, Jr., inspiredly, "it was that doggone duck that Tom and Willie Farrier got at the market last month. They tole me it got away and that ole Tar Beach was raising cain 'cause it like to killed some of his chickens."

"Lord, I might have known it came from the Farriers!" cried Mrs. Multin. "I'm going to call that woman up and tell her a few things! The idea of letting something dangerous like that loose in the neighborhood! And you see here, George Junior, if I ever catch you playing with those Farrier boys, I'll . . . I'll tan the hide right offen you!"

She phoned Mrs. Farrier.

"But, Misses Multin," pleaded Mrs. Farrier, "what can I do? The duck escaped last week, and we never have been able to catch him again. I'm terribly sorry, naturally, about Lulu, but this whole duck business has gotten completely out of my control."

"You should never have let your boys get the thing in the first place," was all the comfort Mrs. Multin would give her. "I've a good mind to complain to the police."

That evening Mrs. Farrier went to call on her best friend, rich, old Mrs. Barsdel who lived one block over and two blocks down. She poured out all her woes to Mrs. Barsdel.

Mrs. Barsdel, to Mrs. Farrier's surprise, cackled with unbridled glee. "Why, that's the funniest thing I ever heard tell of!" she exclaimed. "A duck scaring folks so! Haw, haw, haw! Too bad we don't have more of them ducks around here. Might wake people up."

Her unsuppressed enthusiasm for the drake's doings aroused a similar, if not quite as hearty, enthusiasm in Helen Farrier; and Mrs. Farrier went away from her visit to Mrs. Barsdel thinking that perhaps the drake might not be the unadulterated villain she had long considered him.

Mrs. Barsdel herself went to bed that night still cackling intermittently over the muscovy. And, when she arose in the morning, she remembered him again and cackled all over. She ate a large and leisurely breakfast; then, as was her wont, went to her garden to feed her goldfish.

She had the largest and most beautiful goldfish pool in town. It was as big as a wading pool and almost deep enough to swim in. At one end of it there stood a mirrored gazing globe, larger than a man's head. It rested on a slender bronze pillar, and it mirrored the goldfish pool and the entire garden. It was very lovely.

Mrs. Barsdel would have nothing in her pool but Japanese fantails, the pearly colored beauties with huge cloudlike tails, lacy, delicate fins, and scales so minute and transparent that even the intestines within the fish are clearly visible. Her fish were so tame that they would eat from Mrs. Barsdel's fingers, and they always swarmed to the pool top at the first sign of her approach. She loved them very much; she had named each one, and she spent much time talking to them.

So, after a large and leisurely breakfast, Mrs. Barsdel went out in her garden to feed her goldfish. But even as Tar Beach had discovered in his chicken yard and as Mrs. Multin had discovered in her side yard, so also did Mrs. Barsdel discover in her fish pool an intruder.

The muscovy drake rode high on the water with all the aplomb in the world; as methodical as a Chinese fisherman's trained cormorant, he hunted down the goldfish. They could not escape him by seeking refuge in deep water, for he could dive like an otter and his great beak never missed. Mrs. Barsdel was privileged to watch him make his last splendid dive and catch poor Pitty Sing, her final fantail. His craw already bulged with Pitty Sing's fourteen former companions.

The drake rose to the surface with a swirl, Pitty Sing flopping feebly in his beak. He eyed Mrs. Barsdel angrily, threw up his head to swallow Pitty Sing with a gurgling gulp, and hissed at Mrs. Barsdel, treading water and plainly on his guard.

Mrs. Barsdel was a strong-minded woman, not one to be cowed by a duck. She snatched up a convenient garden rake and made for him, intent on slaughter or worse. For some reason, the drake decided against fighting back; instead of returning the attack, he took to the air. He rose from the goldfish pond with the speedy ponderosity of a large amphibian plane, and, as he left it with a grand noisy rush, knocked over the gazing globe with his left wingtip and smashed it to smithereens on the concrete.

Mrs. Barsdel followed in the footsteps of Tar Beach and Mrs. Multin; she called up Helen Farrier, read the riot act, and emptied out vials of wrath.

"An'," yelled Mrs. Barsdel over the telephone in peroration, "when I seen that damn duck swaller poor Pitty Sing an' then bust my mirror ball, why, I could of jest set down an' bawled!"

Mrs. Farrier did weep. The thing was getting to be too much for her, and she gave way to despair. When her sons came in for lunch, though, she had herself more or less under control and decided to go through the whole matter with them again.

"Willie, this just can't go on any further. You and Tom simply have to catch that awful duck and chop off his head or something. I won't have the neighbors call me up every day and scream at me. I just won't have it!"

"But, mamma, we cain't catch him!" Willie wailed. "We been trying our durndest, too. We seen him the other day over to Thompson's grocery trying to get at some chickens Mister Thompson had in a coop there, but, gosh, he flew off 'fore we could get within fifty feet of him. Gosh, mamma, you really oughtta see him now. He can fly just like a eagle or something!"

"I never want to see the beastly thing again!" snorted Mrs. Farrier. "But if you can't catch your own pet duck, I'm going to get somebody that can."

Said Willie scornfully, "I'd like tuh see anybody catch him if we cain't. Who you gonna get?"

"I'm going to get the police," said Mrs. Farrier determinedly. And she went straight to the telephone. Tom and Willie sat very silent; it was the first time their mother had ever had to have recourse to the police. It must be very serious.

After the chief of police talked to Mrs. Farrier, he hung up the receiver and said to a patrolman, "Well, kin you tie that up?"

"What?"

"It's Miz Farrier. She claims her kids had 'em a pet duck. It got loose a while back, and now it's raising hell all over the neighborhood, and ever'body's scared of the thing. She wants us to go get it."

"Shouldn't be no trick to that," said the patrolman.

"Yeh, but kin you imagine anybody so dumb that they got to call the p'lice department to help 'em catch a damn duck?"

"Well, it takes lots uh people to make the world," philosophized the patrolman.

"Horsecollar," said the chief. But he also said, "I guess you better go on over to her place and catch it fer 'em, anyhow."

"Do I git to keep it if I catch it?" asked the patrolman.

"That's up to Miz Farrier," said the chief.

There was a knocking at the Farrier front door. Willie opened it and found a burly, bluecoated policeman.

"Hello, laddie," said the officer. "You the folks with the duck?"

"We hadda duck," admitted Willie timidly, "but it got away."

"Yer the folks I'm looking for, then," said the policeman. "Whur's yer mother?"

"Gosh, you ain't gonna arrest us, are yuh?"

"Haw, haw, haw! Nope. I just come down to catch yer duck fer yuh. I got a reputation on the force fer being the finest duck-catcher west of the Mississippi River, and I got to keep in practice."

So Willie summoned his mother. She told the policeman to be very careful; the drake was accounted to be uncommonly vicious.

"Oh, I'll handle him, m'am," he assured her. "Don't worry 'bout me a-tall. Whatcha want done with him when I git him?"

"Oh, dear, take him away and do anything you like—except return him here!"

"Kin I have him?"

"You certainly can—with my blessing!"

"Well, thanks, Miz Farrier," said the delighted officer. "We ain't et no duck over to our place fer so long that I'm halfway scared the old lady's fergot how to cook 'em. But mebbe she kin git her hand in again."

And he said to the Farrier sons, "How 'bout you two gennelmen showing me the stomping ground of this here renegade, if yer mamma kin spare yuh fer a few minutes?"

"They'll be glad to help any way they can," said Mrs. Farrier. And the boys said, "Gosh, yes!"

Proud to be guides for a uniformed officer with a big revolver, they led him out through the back yard and down the alley.

"It was over there," said Willie, pointing, "that he like to killed George Junior Multin's rabbit."

"Over on that next block," said Tom, also pointing, "is where he ate all Miz Barsdel's goldfish."

"Down here a little ways," said Willie, "is where he killed a lot of old Tar Beach's chickens."

"That duck certainly gets around," said the policeman.

"I never could figger," mused Willie, "what made him get so mean that way all of a sudden. Why, he was just as gentle when we first got him, wasn't he, Tom?"

"Kinda," said Tom.

They were in the alley at the rear of Tar Beach's place, and, just as they arrived there, a roaring noise and a cloud of smoke came from Tar's chicken yard. It was followed by a fancy assortment of profanity.

"I betcha," said Willie, "that's old Tar shooting at the duck again."

"Well, he better watch hisself firing off firearms within the city limits," said the policeman. "It's strictly agin the law. Come on, boys, I wanta talk to that guy."

He pulled open Tar's wooden gate and strode in, followed by the Farriers. Sure enough, there was Tar with a smoking shotgun in his hands. Two tattered, dead plymouth rocks lay at his feet; other bewildered chickens ran all about. And up on the highest peak of Tar's two-story house, the great white muscovy sat and preened his feathers.

"Look a-here," said the policeman sternly, "it's agin the law to shoot guns in town. You oughtta know that."

"'I God," said Tar Beach, "it ain't agin the law to perteck yer own proputty, is it?"

"What d'yuh mean?" asked the policeman.

Tar pointed at the miscreant on his rooftop. "That's what I mean! That's the third time this week that doggoned duck has got at my fryin' hens. I'm gonna kill that son of a bastard if it's the last mortal thing I ever do. Look at him a-settin' there on my house laughin' at me! 'I God, wait'll I reload! I went an' kilt two uh my own fryers on account of I missed him jest now while he was amongst 'em on the ground, but I aim tuh give him both bar'ls this time an' shoot the guts clean outta him."

"Now, wait a minute," said the policeman. "I jest got through tellin' yuh it was agin the law tuh shoot in town, didn't I?"

"Is it agin the law fer *you* to shoot?" demanded Tar.

"Course not. I'm an officer."

"Aw right!" said Tar. "Here." He handed the policeman his shotgun. "Now you shoot him and ever'thing'll be law-abiding an' jim-dandy."

"Well, I dunno," said the policeman, scratching his head. "I ain't never done nothin' like this before. . . . Still an' all, however, I was sent here with orders to git the duck. I guess mebbe it'll be all right. Gimme a couple uh loads, an' I'll knock him offen there fer yuh. I used tuh be a pretty fair hand at duck-shootin'."

Tar fished around in his pockets; then looked sheepish and irritated. "I ain't got no more loads," he said disgustedly. "That musta been the last I had what I touched off jest now."

"Well, how come yuh missed when he was settin' on the ground?"

"I never missed them there hens," said Tar sadly.

Willie had an idea. "Why don'tcha shoot him with your pistol?" he asked the policeman.

"Well," said the officer doubtfully, "it's sorta long range fer hand-gun shootin'."

"Gimme the gun!" cried Tar. "I don't keer how long the range is."

"Nope," said the patrolman. "If there's any more shootin' done, I'm gonna do it."

He took his revolver from its holster, looked at it speculatively, and then at the drake still preening himself on the roof.

"I ain't had much practice lately on account uh pistol loads costin' so doggoned much," he explained, "but mebbe I kin do it. Stand back, you kids; the muzzle blast is bad."

He sighted long and closely, and fired. The drake still preened.

He took the revolver in both hands, sighted still more closely, and fired. The drake still preened.

He rested the revolver against a tree trunk, and fired. The drake still preened.

He lost his temper and fired the three remaining cartridges as fast as he could pull the trigger. The drake still preened.

The policeman sighed and put away his weapon. "Well," he said, "that's that, I reckon."

"What d'yuh mean 'that's that'?" demanded Tar Beach.

"I ain't got no more loads either," explained the cop.

"Well, what d'yuh aim tuh do?"

"I dunno—'less I go back to the station an' git me a rifle."

"Lordy-Lord! You mean go all the way back on foot?"

"Sure. Whatcha think I came here on—the passenger train?"

"'I God," said Tar despairingly, "I dunno what it is, but that there duck has got a jinx on me. The thing ain't nacheral. I shoot at him a-settin' in my own chicken yard an' miss him a mile an' kill two uh my own fryin' hens. You shoot at him on the roof an' miss him six times. Now, there ain't neither of us got ary loads left fer more shootin', an' the gol-danged thing sets up there an' laughs at us. No, sir, that duck ain't nacheral."

"Tell yuh what," said the cop. "I hate tuh be beat by a doggone ornery duck, an' I don't aim tuh be. You all stay here an' watch him. I'll hike back to the station quick as I kin an' git me a rifle. I'm a shore cinch tuh hit him with a rifle, even if I cain't with a doggone six-shooter."

"Yeh, but you got ary reason tuh believe he's a-gonna set there an' wait fer yuh to fetch a rifle all the way back here?"

"Well, that's why I want you all tuh watch him. You can sorta foller him if he takes a notion to go somewhere er other. Honest, it's the only thing I kin think of."

"Well, it hain't much of an idear," said Tar scornfully.

Willie broke in, saying excitedly, "Hey, look at the duck now, wouldja?"

They all looked. The drake was standing up on his big flat feet, apparently through for the day with his preening. He looked insolently down at his foes and shook himself. He thrust out first one wing, then the other, stretching them leisurely. Then he flapped both wings violently, as if to make sure they were in good working order.

"Looks like," said Tar, "he's already got his notion to go somewhere er other."

"Well, I cain't think of no way off hand to stop him," said the cop.

The muscovy walked slowly along the roof till he reached its very edge. There, majestically, he launched himself into the air, falling nearly twenty feet before his thrashing pinions took hold. Then he climbed with massive wing-beats above the level of the neighborhood roofs. He circled Tar Beach's back yard twice, rising higher and higher, then headed west and went lumbering out of sight with the grace of a threshing machine.

"Mebbe he's gone fer good," said the cop optimistically.

"Mebbe," said Tar.

"I done the best I could, anyhow," said the cop.

"Well, I sure thank yuh fer yer help," said Tar.

"I 'spect I better be gettin' on back, though," said the cop. "So long, you kids. Tell yer mother I done the best I could."

"Yeh, we will," said the Farriers. They left, too. "Good-by, Mister Beach."

" 'By, boys," said Tar absently. He went over and picked up his two dead frying hens.

Back at the station, the chief asked the patrolman about reports coming in of much shooting in the neighborhood where the patrolman had been sent to catch the duck.

"That must of been me," said the cop. "I fired a time er two."

"Didja git him?" asked the chief.

"Nope, but I sure scared hell out of him."

Three days after the policeman's efforts, Mrs. Farrier was sitting on her front porch, sewing and rocking. A big green farm wagon stopped in the street in front. From it, after he twisted the reins around the brake handle, alighted a large, genial-looking man in overalls. He came to the porch step and took off his hat. "Are you Miz Farrier?" he asked politely.

"Yes."

"Well, I'm Mister Renfro; I live out towards Muddy Creek a ways."

"Yes?"

"Well, some time back, I think it was your two boys who bought a duck offen me at the market."

"Oh, dear! Now what's happened?"

"Why, nothing much. 'Cept this morning I thought I seen that duck I sold your kids back in with my others, and I was wondering if he could of got away from yuh or something. If he did, I'll be more'n glad to return him."

"No! No!" cried Mrs. Farrier. "It's not our duck. There's been a mistake. We don't want any ducks. We don't like ducks."

"Well, but, ma'am, if he's yourn, looks like you'd want him back."

"No!" said Mrs. Farrier. "We don't want him. Please don't bring any ducks around here. Please!"

"Well . . . okay," said Mr. Renfro. "I jest thought I'd ask, on account of being in town today. Mebbe I'm a duck to the good."

He left somewhat bewildered.

Mrs. Farrier fiddled around uncertainly for a while and then decided that the occasion demanded some unusual manifestation in the way of celebrating. She made a hurried trip to town and then busied herself in the kitchen. When Tom and Willie came trooping in, asking about supper, they were startled to the soles of their shoes to see ice cream and cake on the table.

WHO WAS JOE MILLER?

◆§ ROBERT O. FOOTE

Humor, say philosophers, is the index of an era's sophistication. Because the present day laughs at broad jokes, it is inclined to fancy itself as tolerant; "modern" is the popular word. The stories we tell in mixed company would only have been whispered by grandfather to his barroom cronies. Ipso facto, we're pretty darn sophisticated. But are we?

Examine a case example: You see a cartoon—or will shortly when the gag men realize what they have been overlooking—which shows a young man getting out of bed in which still reposes a lovely dame. The caption says "I think I'll get up and rest."

Now, except for the manner of its telling through the aid of a drawing reproduction process unknown to our ancestors, instead of completely by words as was necessary with them, that is the identical joke at which our forebears of two hundred years ago were snickering. Here is its exact wording, No. 164 in the now priceless first edition of *Joe Miller's Jests*:

"A Young Lady who had been Married but a Short Time, seeing her Husband going to Rise pretty early in the Morning, said, 'What, my Dear, are you getting up already? Pray lie a little longer and rest yourself.' 'No, my Dear,' replied the husband, 'I'll get up and rest myself.'"

Even then it was an old joke, like all of Joe Miller's, of whom more anon, as he would say. It is cited here merely as a single demonstration, among hundreds of possible ones, that the love of what the Puritan calls "dirty jokes" is firmly implanted in the Anglo-Saxon. The Jest Books which are treasured possessions of the great libraries were the *Esquires* and *New Yorkers* of the 15th, 16th, 17th centuries, until nasty niceness forced them onto the back shelves for more than one hundred years.

68

Those ancient tomes afford rewarding research to a man who, like the late Justice Oliver W. Holmes, finds the facts of life and the expression thereof rather amusing. Their study and the tracing of their relationship with the now happily emancipated laughter of the present has been the favorite relaxation of this writer for years.

While there is no record of any joke book having been compiled in English prior to the invention of printing, that innovation was applied to the service of laughter even before it came to the aid of piety. The first complete Bible in our language was that issued by Miles Coverdale in 1535; almost ten years before that, in 1526, there was issued the first jest book, called *C Mery Tayls*.

This *Hundred Merry Tales* (to translate its title into our spelling) is one of the rarest of all books, there are only two known copies. Great Britain possesses one, badly mutilated. The other is a perfect copy that reposes in the Library of the University of Guttingen, which bears this legend on its title page:

"Emprynted at London at the Sign of the Merymayd at Powlys Gate next to Chepesyde. The Year of our Lorde MDXXVI: the XXII day of November."

One fourth of its jokes would be unprintable, even by our relaxed standards. That is a fair approximation of the proportion of overly risqué that persisted in the humorous literature of the following two hundred years. Yet examination of copies of that earliest jest book, which have reached this country, reveals that its conviction that marriage is an essentially comic matter to all but the victims, would easily pass current as keen wit in this day. Here is a specimen:

"A man asked his neighbor which was but late married to a widow how he agreed with his wife, for he said that her first husband and she could never agree. 'By God, quoth the other, we agree marvelous well.' 'I pray thee how so?' 'I shall tell you, quoth the other, when I am merry she is merry and when I am sad she is sad, for when I go out of my doors I am merry to go from her and so is she and when I come in again I am sad and so is she.'"

A fascinating perusal of many old jest books reveals that the early years of each succeeding century seem to have been especially fruitful in laughter. In 1526 came *C Mery Tayls*. In 1633 or thereabouts came John Taylor, the Water Poet, and Archie Armstrong, King Charles I's jester, to lend a terser and slightly cleaner tinge to the humor of the people. In 1739 came Joe Miller, to act as stepfather to all the earlier smiles. By about the middle of the 1800's appear Mark Lemon in England and Artemus Ward in America, signifying a sad falling off in the soul of wit. In the 1920's there was a speeding up of sophistication in the humor of America and a return to the frankness of four hundred years previously.

Most of these old books are extremely rare and there is a constant search for them. Among the finest collection in America, though not segregated even there, are the handsome specimens of original John Taylors, Archie Armstrongs, Joe Millers and many others among the treasures of the Henry E. Huntington Library in California.

Archie was the most urbane of the early jesters. His stories told in 1633 and 1639 are not only an improvement in expression and point over those of earlier date, they also excel those which were perpetrated a hundred years later in the notorious name of Joe Miller.

There is a modern twist to much of Archie's humor. The popular gag of one favorite cartoonist of today, that of having a husband, or wife, thinking of something else all the time the other is engaged in telling a long-winded yarn, harks back directly to Archie's tale of:

"One making a long and tedious speech to a grave counselor on the conclusion thereof made an apologie to excuse himself for being so troublesome; who gave him answer, I'll assure you, sir, you have not been troublesome to me at all, for all the time you were speaking my mind was of another matter."

There were Farmer's Daughters in humor nearly four hundred years ago. Indeed, it is possible to trace with almost exactitude the time that she stepped into folklore. In that first jest book of 1526 is a story of a bridegroom who was forced to allow his bride to wait at the church, while at the instigation of the irate father of another sweetheart he made a pecuniary settlement upon the previous object of his affections. The point of the tale is that the bride, upon later wheedling the facts out of her new husband, proved herself above small reproaches. She was content to comment that the girl had been foolish to betray the affair to her father. She, the bride, had been carrying on, she said, in like fashion with a man-servant for a year but her husband was now the first person to whom she had ever made it known.

When the tale reappears a century later in *Archie's Jests* of 1639 (and much better told) the deceived sweetheart has become not simply the "mayd" she was in the earlier version, but a "Farmer's Daughter"—her first appearance as a stock character of ribald wit.

It took intense, but extremely captivating research, much bur-rowing into the treasures of ancient libraries for this inquirer to fix, even within a hundred years, that important date in the his-tory of humor. Many men have gone honored to their graves for lesser achievements.

Once embarked, however, upon such a research project, no true student could let the matter drop. It went on and on, eventually bringing the conviction that the Elizabethans recognized the es-sentials of lasting humor exactly as we do. To every age its own language; to all the ages the same fundamental risibility.

Their primary conviction was that the fact of there being two sexes was quite a joke upon humanity; exactly the same imperish-able joke to be found in the last issue of any smart magazine. Many of the jests of those gusty early Englishmen were sadly naïve. Their practical jokes, their execrable puns, their witty re-torts, their puncturing of ostentation, take a decided sharpening up for modern taste, though it is being done daily, in print and on the air. But when they wanted a belly laugh they went to the relationship of the sexes, just as we do.

Whether or not we do it any better is a matter of opinion, tak-ing into consideration the fact that our ancestors could not illus-trate their jests. Here is one from which you may draw your own conclusions. Archie first committed it to print:

"A Scholar having married a young wife and being still at his book, preferring his serious study before dalliance with her; as she was one day sitting lonely, whilst he was reading, 'Sir,' saith she, 'I would with myself I had been a book, for then you would be still pouring over me and I would never, night or day, be without your attention.' 'So would I, sweetheart,' answered he, 'so I might choose the book.' To whom she again answered, 'And what book would you wish me to be?' 'Sweetheart,' saith he, 'an almanack for so I might have a new one every year.' "

To trace the development of such tales, which now appear again as the "very latest—stop me if you've heard it before," is a rare delight. Most such yarns, particularly the bawdy ones, have been printed over and over, down the centuries. Occasionally a squawk is raised over joke-stealing. It is not actual theft, the joke always belongs to the last person who tells it, if he can improve upon it, so much the better. That, at least, was the admirable attitude of John Taylor in his *Wit and Mirth* published 313 years ago, when he said in his preface:

"Because I have had many of these tales by relation and hearsay, I am in doubt that some of them may be in print in some other authors, which I do assure you is more than I do know; which if it be so, I pray you to tolerate and let the authors make twice as bold with me at any time."

Since it is not the happy lot of all to be able to pursue from original source such an entrancing research as this, it would seem to be doing a distinct service at this point to offer some of the early versions from which matrimonial favorites have been drawn. So, slightly purified as to language, with the spelling modernized for ease in reading, here is, as the old title pages used to say, "A Choice Banquet of Jests":

The Emperor Augustus, being shown a young Grecian who very much resembled him, asked the Young Man if his Mother had not been at Rome. "No, sir," answered the Grecian, "but my Father has."—*Joe Miller, 1739.*

A young Gentleman playing at Questions and Commands with some very pretty young Ladies, was commanded to take off the Garter from one of them; but she, as soon as he had laid hold of her Petticoats, ran away into the next Room, "Now, Madam," said he, tripping up her heels, "I bar squealing." "Bar the door, you fool," cry'd she.—*Joe Miller, 1739.*

A handsome Wench, for some suspicious business, being brought before a Justice somewhat late in the evening and he taking compassion of her because she was fair and seeming modest, wished the man that brought her before him, to take her home and lodge her that night and he would hear the case more at length in the morning: "With all my heart," saith the man, "Master Justice, so you will commit my wife, which is now at home, to the jail till the morning."—*Archie's Jests, 1639.*

Upon a time Tarlton and His wife, as passengers, came sailing towards London a mighty storm arose and endangered the ship, whereupon the captain charged every man to throw into the seas the heaviest thing he could best spare, to the end to lighten somewhat the ship. Tarlton, that had his wife there, offered to throw her overboard; but the company rescued her and being asked wherefore he meant so to do, he answered "She is the heaviest thing I have and I can best spare her."—*Tarlton's Jests, 1570.*

A Waiting Gentlewoman being summoned into a Court to take an oath, the Examiner asked her how he should write her down: a Maid, a Wife or a Widow? She told him he should write her down a Maid, for she never had any husband. He finding her a pretty handsome smug Wench, asked her how old she was; she told him about the age of six and twenty: saith he (willing to sport with her), "Then take heed what you swear, for you are now upon your oath and therefore may I securely set you down Maid, being of those years?" The Wench made a pause and considered a while with herself: "I pray you, sir," saith she, "stay your hand a little and write me down a Young Woman."—*Archie, 1639.*

A Company of Rustics, having taken a Wolf, consulted on some exquisite torment, which one of them presently thought of: "Let him," saith he, "be married to two wifes as I am and hell itself can add no greater torment."—*Archie, 1633.*

A woman in Scotland lay dying, to whom her husband said, "Wife, now thou art about to leave me alone, I pray thee tell me with whom I shall marry?" She replied, "Art thou in haste to marry before the breath be out of my body, then marry the devil's dam." "Not so, Wife," saith he, "I have his daughter already an I should mate with his mother too, then I should be guilty of incest."—*John Taylor, 1629.*

This sort of stuff demonstrates that humor has changed less in the last four hundred years than in a thousand previous years. Joe Miller, despite the popular assumption of the contrary opinion, was not the first man to collect ancient wheezes. The very first of whom there is record was one Hierocles of the Fifth Century, about whose exact identity scholars still quarrel but about whose list of twenty-one alleged jokes there can be little dispute—they are the foundation of the most ghastly wit in all creation. Suffer through a few of the least intolerable; you probably have heard their revision within the last month on the air:

A scholar wishing to teach his horse to eat little, gave him no food at all; and the horse dying, "How unlucky," said he, "as soon as I had taught him to live without food, he died."

Another meaning to sell a house, carried about a stone of it as a specimen.

A pedant sealed a wine vessel he had, but his man bored the bottom and stole the liquor. He was astonished at the liquor's diminishing, though the seal was entire; and another saying, "Perhaps it is taken out at the bottom," the pedant answered, "Most foolish of men, it is not the under part but the upper part that is deficient."

A man hearing that crows lived two hundred years, bought one, saying, "I wish to make the experiment."

A scholar meeting a person, said to him, "I heard you were dead." To which the other answered, "You see I am alive." The scholar replied, "Perhaps so, but he who told me was a man of much more credit than you."

Hearing that one of two twins was dead, when he met the other, a scholar asked, "Which of you was it that died? You or your brother."

A scholar in Greece receiving a letter from a friend desiring him to buy some books there, neglected the business. But the friend arriving some time after, the scholar said, "I am sorry I did not receive your letter about the books."

This latter is one of the standard jokes of the world, in every age and every language. Joe Miller's version of it is hung upon an Irish lawyer who left this note for his servant: "I am gone to the Elephant and Castle where you shall find me and if you can't read this Note, carry it down to the Stationer's and he will read it for you."

Which brings us back to the most famous of all humorists and the least deserving of the title. Over two hundred years ago an enterprising publisher gave to the English reading world its most universally accepted designation for an old joke—a "Joe Miller."

Too dead to resist, Joe Miller had immortality thrust upon him. He was a fairly popular actor who had died the previous year. Following the custom of the times, his name was hung upon the next London collection of supposedly funny stories, most of which he probably never had heard. The book, *Joe Miller's Jests*, became upon its publication in 1739 the first best seller on record and it has had the longest run in history. It is still being reissued, in modern guise. Joe Miller's chestnuts are never so stale but a re-roasting will revive their flavor.

THE FREE LANCE

⊷ WOLCOTT GIBBS

Mr. Andrew Eppley president of the Municipal Bureau of Subways, stood at the window of his office, looking forty-seven stories down into the street. For two days some men had been doing something to the paving, and now there was a raw cavity which reached almost from curb to curb. It was surrounded by machinery and tar-paper shacks, and both ends of the street itself were barred with trestles. At night lanterns traced a red geometry in the canyon; by day the nervous chattering of the drills floated thinly up to Mr. Eppley, even on his splendid heights.

"What you suppose them babies doing down there, Joey?" Mr. Eppley asked his secretary, Miss Murphy, without turning around.

"Laying sewer pipe, prolly," she replied, for this with her was a sort of generic explanation of all the awful mysteries that go on beneath the city.

"Yeah, well, it don't look like no sewer pipe to *me*," said Mr. Eppley, tipping dangerously over the sill to see better. "You know what it looks like to me, Joey? It looks like them babies might be doing the digging for a subway. We ain't got a subway coming out no place down here, have we?"

"I don't remember," she said.

"Listen, sweetheart," said Mr. Eppley, "you ain't getting paid for remembering. How about looking in the maps and *seeing* where we got our subways coming out?"

"Oh, all *right*," she said wearily and, putting down her *Modern Priscilla*, she took her small, agreeable shape off to a corner of the office, where there was a long battery of files. Here she was angrily busy for some time, banging drawers and scuffing through folders.

"Nope," she said finally. "We ain't got a subway within ten blocks."

Perhaps it should be explained here that almost the first thing Tammany did upon its return to power in 1942 was to take all the subways out of private hands, and convert them into a department of the city government. There were, of course, a great many worthy candidates for the presidency of this important bureau, but it was finally decided that Mr. Eppley's martyrdom for the Cause (in 1936 he had served a short term, convicted on a false and cowardly charge of ballot-box-stuffing), combined with his long experience in the house-wrecking game, entitled him to first consideration, and he was appointed by a unanimous vote. Thereafter all subway construction and operation had been under his jurisdiction, and all plans, naturally, were, or should have been, in his files.

Mr. Eppley looked down again at the hole in the street.

"It certainly *looks* like they was doing the digging for a subway," he said thoughtfully. "Look, Joey, see can you get the Mayor on the phone."

"My!" she said admiringly.

"Never mind about that," said Mr. Eppley. "You get him."

"O.K." she said. "Don't get overwrought."

"And listen, Joey, you better talk to him. Maybe it would put in a better appearance. What I want to find out, see, is have they got a record of this subway down at City Hall. Maybe we got some mistake in our files. I mean, it would look like hell if it turned out we really *was* building a subway through this street and I didn't know nothing about it. Get what I mean?"

"Sure," she said, "like the time you had the boys digging up Jones Beach instead of Jones Street."

"Never mind," said Mr. Eppley. "Anyways, don't ask him right out, see? Just hint around, like you was kidding. Or, wait a minute"—he chuckled—"I got it. Tell him I gone out of town—maybe with a dame, see?—and I took all these important papers with me so that you don't know *where* the hell we got subways. Tell him you got to know right off, because you got some important guy on another line, waiting. That would let us out all right, wouldn't it?"

"It lets *you* out," she said bitterly. "It don't make me look any too bright, though."

"All right, all right," he said. "Get going."

Sulkily, she began to dial, and presently was indeed talking to the Mayor. Mr. Eppley listened anxiously but could make little out of the one-sided conversation.

"Well," he said, when she had hung up, "what'd he say?"

"He says there ain't no subway nearer here than Broad Street," she told him, and added pleasantly, "He wants to know how long you going to be canned up *this* time."

"Ain't *that* nice, after all I done for that guy?" demanded Mr. Eppley, but he was too troubled for indignation, and wandered again to the window.

"If that ain't a subway, I'm Linboigh," he said unhappily.

Miss Murphy was about to reply when a buzzer sounded on her desk. She picked up the inter-office phone and listened.

"Guy to see you," she said finally. "Name of Edmunds. It's about subways."

"What about subways?"

"Miss Burns asked him, but he wouldn't say," she said. "Just about subways, he told her."

"All right, get him in," said Mr. Eppley. "I might as well talk to somebody as go nuts worrying."

"That's right," said Miss Murphy. "Show Mr. Edmunds in," she said to the telephone.

Mr. Edmunds came in at an anxious trot. He was a little man, with misty eyes in a face almost obliterated by fine, silky hair. His clothes struck a sort of low-comedy balance because while his derby hat was much too small and rode high above his flanking ears, his sleeves and the legs of his trousers were much too long, so that his fingers and the toes of his shoes were visible only shyly and intermittently when he made some sudden movement. He carried a tattered briefcase and a badly rolled umbrella.

"Are you Mr. Eppley?" he asked diffidently. "I'm Paul Edmunds."

"Pleased to meet you," said Mr. Eppley. "Sit down. Take a powder, Joey."

The door closed behind her, and Mr. Eppley's caller bent across the desk.

"Mr. Eppley," he said, "I'm afraid I'm coming to you with rather a peculiar proposition."

"It ain't insurance, is it?" asked Mr. Eppley. "Because if it is—"

"Oh, no," said the stranger, drawing back in horror. "It certainly isn't insurance."

"*Nor* books. I don't need no books. I got my hands full up with what I'm doing right here."

"Oh, no. To tell the truth"—he laughed uneasily—"I don't know just how to tell you about the proposition I want to make you because, as I said, it *is so very* peculiar."

"Yeah?" said Mr. Eppley.

"Yes, in*deed*. You see, Mr. Eppley, I've always been a rather inventive sort of chap. Always doing things with my hands. Even when I was just a shaver in Flushing, my parents tried over and over to make me go out and play games—rugger and, er, other sporting events—but I always preferred to stay in my little tool-shop and, well, just *tinker. Chacun à son gout,* you know."

"Right," said Mr. Eppley.

"Well, it kept on right through school and college—I was Harvard '13. Perhaps you are a Harvard man, Mr. Eppley? . . . No? Well, anyway, all through my life, where other fellows might turn to books or the theatre or the, ah, flowing bowl, it was machinery with me. You might say machinery was my mistress. In a way, of course."

"You liked locomotive engines and all, you mean?" said Mr. Eppley.

"Something like that. Well, when I came to New York last year —and here we come to my point—I said to myself, now what is the most exciting thing a man could do in this great wonderful city? What would I like to do most? And what do you suppose I said, Mr. Eppley?"

"You got me," confessed Mr. Eppley.

"Subways! Paul, I said to myself, *that's* the job for you! Subways! Tunnelling under those great buildings, through the granite and sand and water, so that all those hurrying millions could get to and fro just a little more comfortably and quickly. It seemed to me the greatest career in the world, and I promised myself I wouldn't rest until—"

"I'm sorry, Mr. Edmunds," said Mr. Eppley, who thought he saw a light, "but we ain't got any jobs here just at the moment. Things are pretty slow right now, what with the lousy Board of Estimate raising a stink every time a man tries to order a carload of fishplate. Why, only last week—"

"Ah, but I don't think you quite understand me, Mr. Eppley," said Mr. Edmunds gently. "I'm not asking you for a job."

"No? Then—"

"No. I already have my dream. I *am* a subway builder, Mr. Eppley!"

"You're *what?*"

"I *am* a subway builder! I *have* built a subway!"

"Where!" asked Mr. Eppley, but he had already begun to tingle with a horrid presentiment.

"I'll show you," said Mr. Edmunds, and he got up and skipped over to Mr. Eppley's window. "I wonder if you'd mind stepping over here just a minute, Mr. Eppley?"

Mr. Eppley followed him.

"There it is," said Mr. Edmunds, and pointed, as Mr. Eppley had been miserably sure he would, at that toiling ant heap so far below.

"I see," said Mr. Eppley dully.

"It took capital and it took ingenuity," said Mr. Edmunds proudly. "You have no idea how, well, *cluttered* New York is underneath. But it's the longest subway in the world and the straightest. Runs from the Battery clear up to Yonkers without a curve. What do you think of that?"

"It's something, all right," said Mr. Eppley. "Say, who knows about this thing, anyways?"

"Oh, hardly anybody except the men I hired," said Mr. Edmunds. "I rather dispensed with the formalities. Just decided to dig it and went right ahead. Of course there were mistakes—we couldn't hope to avoid a cellar here and there—but on the whole it went quietly."

"It certainly did," said Mr. Eppley.

"Be finished tomorrow unless something goes wrong," said Mr. Edmunds, "and that brings me again to why I came to see you. As I told you, Mr. Eppley, I'm a creative sort of beggar. As soon as I finish one job—bing!—I want to be off and away and at something else. Off with the old, on with the new. That sort of thing."

"Oh, sure," said Mr. Eppley feebly.

"The point is, though, it's a little difficult to focus on a new project until the old one is cleared up. What I wanted to ask you, Mr. Eppley, is just this: how does one go about disposing of a subway? I asked several people—putting it to them as a purely hypothetical case, of course—and they all mentioned you. And that," he finished triumphantly, "is really why I'm here."

Mr. Eppley looked at Mr. Edmunds for a long time.

"You want to sell me this subway?" he asked, at length.

"Well, yes," said Mr. Edmunds. "I could really let you have it very cheaply—for what it cost me, practically. You see, I do these things mostly for the fun of it. Of course, I don't like to work for nothing—what do they say about the laborer being worthy of his hire?—but the actual amount hardly matters at all."

There was another long silence, while Mr. Eppley tapped a

pencil on his desk and stared out of the window. Finally his face seemed to clear.

"I tell you what, Mr. Edmunds," he said, "you got a mighty interesting little proposition there, a mighty interesting and un-usual little proposition, and I want to think about it. You and me can make a deal all right, but I want to think about it. You know, like the details. What you do, you leave me your name and ad-dress, and I'll get in touch with you."

"When?" demanded Mr. Edmunds, who had a sort of meek ob-stinacy.

"Tomorrow, or the next day at the latest," said Mr. Eppley. "But you'll certainly hear from me."

Mr. Edmunds sorted a rumpled card out of the confusion of papers in his pocket and handed it to Mr. Eppley.

"That's fine," he said, getting up. "That's awfully good of you, Mr. Eppley."

"It ain't nothing," said Mr. Eppley politely. "You'll hear from me. So long."

"*Au'voir*," said Mr. Edmunds.

As soon as the door had closed behind Mr. Edmunds, Mr. Ep-pley rang for Miss Murphy.

"Listen, Joey," he said nervously, "don't let that guy in here no more. I don't care what he says, just don't let him *in* no more. You got that?"

"O.K.," she said calmly, "but what's the matter with him? He looked like a nice little guy to me."

"Yeah," said Mr. Eppley, "he's a nice little guy, but he's nuts, that's what's the matter with him."

Even as he spoke a feather of sound, the faintest whisper from those faraway drills, curled in at the window, and Mr. Eppley shivered.

"He's nuts," repeated Mr. Eppley, but he didn't believe it for a minute.

MARY, QUEEN OF SCOTS

☙ GUY GILPATRIC

The *Inchcliffe Castle,* Para to Naples, stuck her rusty snout around the bend of Andalucia and ambled into sheltered waters across which sprawled the purple shadow of Gibraltar. Behind the Rock the sun had climbed an hour high; but Britannia's Lion, in its towering majesty, shut off all save a few ambitious rays which leaked around its edges, and framed it in a pinkly glowing aureole.

The full moon, on the other hand—it would have been your left—swung over the white houses of Algeciras, in Spain, and sinking lower, paved a baleful pathway beyond Trafalgar for the wandering footsteps of Admiral Nelson's unquiet, lovesick ghost.

In this strange and lovely moment of borning day and dying night, the *Inchcliffe Castle's* anchor let go with a shocking clatter of chains, a vulgar display of sparks, much profanity from the fo'c'sle head and even more from the bridge. The profanity was that of religious men, which is the kind that blisters paint.

The anchor caught in the mud, jerked loose once or twice, stirred up many bubbles and an evil smell, and finally hooked a fluke. Mr. Montgomery, hanging over the bow and seeing the chain stretch taut, waved his hands with the weary yet triumphant gesture of an orchestra leader bringing the Ninth Symphony to a glorious close.

Captain Ball, on the bridge, heaved a stertorous sigh. "Ring off the engines," he directed; and somewhere down below, the telegraph jingled. Suddenly, disturbingly, the decks ceased to throb and the stanchions to tremble. After eighteen pulsing days the ship seemed no longer to be alive. Silence, torrents of silence, poured in from all sides. And just then the sun, conquering the traditionally unconquerable, scaled Gibraltar's heights and sent the night, its moon, and its lovely mystery scurrying away into Africa.

"Hell's bones!" remarked Captain Ball, unbottoning his overcoat and taking a cigar from his night-shirt pocket. "What a trip *that* was!" Resting his elbows on the bridge rail, his eye travelled aft over the battered gear and salt-streaked superstructure which told of a rough and troublous passage.

Mr. Glencannon, the Chief Engineer, appeared on the deck below. At the heels of his oil-soaked carpet slippers toddled a jet black female Scottish terrier with barrel chest, stump legs, and whiskers such as one associates with natives of Aberdeen. Mr. Glencannon strolled to the rail, spat copiously over it, and considered Gibraltar at length—meanwhile wiping his face with a handful of greasy cottonwaste. Then he lifted the dog in his arms, and placed her forepaws on the rail.

"Mary," he said, "this is Geebraltar, an heestoric port. I'll first deerect your attention to the street which runs peerpindicular to yon wharf. If ye'll note the fourth—no, the fufth building on the left, ye'll be notin' a pub whuch sells the finest whusky South of the Firth o' Clyde. And then, on the nuxt street, over toward the naval coal docks, ye'll see a sma' house wi' a red roof. That's a pub called 'The Royal Oak,' after an old ancient freegate ship whuch . . . oh, a vurra gude morning to you, Captain Ball!"

"Good morning, Mr. Glencannon," and the Captain nodded over the canvas dodger. "How are you and Mary this morning—fit?"

Mr. Glencannon shook his head dolefully. "As fur my ain puir health, the less said the better. But Mary, the little lass, is ailin' sore. I was aboot to crave yer kind permeesion, Sir, to tak' her ashoor to a vetereenary, and get him to preescribe."

"Right-o," agreed the Captain cheerfully.

"Thanks kindly, Captain Ball," said Mr. Glencannon, setting Mary on the deck and deftly brushing up her coat. "The lass and I are grateful. We are indeed. Come on, Sweetheart—we'll ha' a bit o' brukfust, we will, and then Papa'll put on his new uneefurrm, and dress his ain little lass in her tartan collar, and hoot! ashore for a romp we'll go!"

"Oh, now, my eye!" exploded Mr. Montgomery, the mate, who

had joined Captain Ball upon the bridge. "Did you ever 'ear such blithering tosh in all your life, Sir?—Mr. Glencannon mykes a bit of an arss of 'imself over that dog when 'e sets 'is mind to it, 'e does!"

Captain Ball crinkled the corners of his eyes as do men who weren't born yesterday. "Well, I'll tell you, Mr. Montgomery, it's like this. I know as well as you do that he's going ashore to get drunk. Mr. Glencannon has his weaknesses, as who of us does not? Scripture says that 'To sin is human,' and though Mr. Glencannon drinks a full quart of whisky everyday, and be damned if I haven't seen him drink five quarts, we must remember to let he without sin cast the first stone.—Particularly when he's the only Engineer on the high seas who can handle our rusty old tubercular junk pile of a blank-blanked engine."

"Well, all I can say is, God 'elp the Rock of Gibraltar!" grunted Mr. Montgomery, only half convinced. " 'Ere'e comes now."

Mr. Glencannon, brave in his best white cap, the four gold stripes of his rank, and the medal awarded him for saving a German's life by mistake, stood at the foot of the gangway and invited bids from the yammering bumboatmen to take him ashore. He cut the lowest bid in half, kicked the chin of the nearest competitor, who had sought to seize his arm, and made the trip to the Commercial Wharf for thruppence. With Mary frisking at his heels, he passed through cobbled streets lined with whitewashed houses labelled, for example, "*Sgt. Major Alfred Hoskins, 67th Rgt. R.G.A.*," and "*Non-Com. Married Quarters—No Loitering.*" The latter sign he felt to be distinctly offensive in its insinuation. "Ha' no fear!" he muttered toward it. "I've better to do than loiter aboot with the she-beef o' the Royal Garrison Arteelery!" And forthwith he turned into an establishment the window of which displayed a spirited lithograph of the Relief of Lucknow, depicting several bottles of MacCrimmon's Very Old Liqueur Whisky being put to good use by the beleaguered defenders in the foreground.

He found MacCrimmon's Very Old to be distinctly creditable stuff—as good, in some respects, as The Laird's Selected Relics, Clammarty Royal Tartan Blend and Dunleven Particularly Choice. But none of them, of course, could compare with Duggan's Dew of Kirkintilloch—most gorgeous of all liquids that ever dripped golden from the nozzle of a still to mingle its perfume with that of the heather in the cold Highland mists.

Now, like Duggan's Dew, Mr. Glencannon hailed from the town of Kirkintilloch, in Dumbartonshire; and the picture on the label made him first happy, then sentimental, and finally homesick. A great grief overcame him; tears coursed his cheeks as he contemplated that label, and he was weeping copiously when he finished the bottle. "Look," he sobbed, hoisting Mary to the table, "Gaze, Lass, upon the dear fameeliar scenes o' your childhood! 'Tis there that our Mothers live. Ye played there as a bairn, and so, alas, did I. . . ." And Mary, falling into the spirit of the occasion, tilted back her head and gave vent to piercing wails. Mr. Glencannon purchased six cases of the whisky, ordered five to be delivered aboard the ship and the sixth to be stowed in a cab. The cab proved to be a spidery victoria driven by a Spaniard in straw hat, short jacket and baggy trousers. Mr. Glencannon and Mary scrambled aboard with the God-speed of the publican and some assistance from the by-standers.

"Where to, Capitan?" inquired the Spaniard.

"How in the hell shud I know?" replied Mr. Glencannon. "Must I act as guide to ye, on ye're ain native heath?"

"But I come from La Linea, Senor," protested the Spaniard.

"Vurra weel—let's go there, then," and with Mary perched on the seat beside him, Mr. Glencannon dropped off to sleep.

They had clip-clopped out of the streets of the town and were well in sight of the Neutral Strip—a barb-wired belt of land which separates Spain from the Crown Colony of Gibraltar— when the driver reined in his nag. Mr. Glencannon, opening his eyes, saw that they were halted at a house before which paced a sentry in the uniform of the Royal Garrison Artillery. A sign on the place read "*H.Q. Frontier Guard. Passes for Spain.*" Across the road, under the flat face of the Rock, stretched a field filled with hurdles, water-jumps, cricket greens, polo goal posts, and aeroplane hangars. Upon this field, troops were playing football.

The driver dismounted, entered the house, and shortly emerged with a little green slip which read "North front. Permit until first evening gunfire. John Cochrane, Chief of Frontier Police."

Mr. Glencannon was considering this suspiciously, and was just about to ask Mary what country they were in, when a disturbing sound came from the distance. At first he thought he only imagined it, and instinctively he glanced at Mary for confirmation. But yes—her ears were cocked, her tail was wagging, and she was craning her neck around the side of the carriage. It was the sound of bagpipes; and they were playing "Piobair o' Lochaber."

"Foosh!" exclaimed Mr. Glencannon, lurching to his feet. "Why, it's the Argyll and Dumbarton Highlanders!" Mary showed her front teeth in a broad smile and then her entire perfect set in a series of joyous barks. Her little hairy forepaws pattered on the cushions, and she wriggled with excitement. For there, down the long white road, was the head of the approaching column—kilts and sporrans swinging to the time, white gaiters slogging up and down, tartan ribbons aflutter on the pipes, and the bass-drummer with his leopard-skin apron whirling his sticks cross-armed, overhead, and behind him in the wild inimitable Highland manner!— It was the Dumbartons, beyond a doot—and Mr. Glencannon's own Cousin Douglas was a Sergeant of the Regiment!

Nearer and nearer they came—the shrill chant and basso drone of the pipes leaping into the air and echoing against the great grey face of the Rock above the plain. Then came the muffled *clump* of sixteen hundred hobnailed boots, the rhythmic swish of eight hundred tartan kilts! The Dumbartons—the great and glorious Dumbartons!—were marching by! Wheeling smartly before his very carriage, they deployed into the field.

They were going to play football, and so they weren't carrying their rifles. Numerous sporting Majors, Captains and Subalterns had turned out with the team, and they swung along with their walking sticks beneath their arms and banter upon their lips. And over all, there was a friendly, comfortable smell of venerable Scotch whisky upon the soft Iberian air. . . .

Mr. Glencannon was sniffing deep when suddenly he and Mary beheld a sight which transfixed them. It was the regimental mascot—the handsomest, whiskeriest Scottish terrier in the whole wide world—a rakish, swashbuckling lad wearing a tiny Highland bonnet cocked over one ear, the silver-and-cairngorm badge of the Dumbartons pinned to the side of it. And he toddled along with a man who stood full seven feet high—a giant with a chest the size of the *Inchcliffe Castle's* main boiler, and great hairy knees like the oak trees worshipped by the Druids of antiquity. This giant—there could be no mistaking him!—was Mr. Glencannon's own Cousin Douglas.

Mary cast virginal modesty to the winds, and shrilly yapped her admiration. Cousin Douglas, spotting Mr. Glencannon, gave vent to a joyous "Hoot!" and promptly fell out of the ranks. Mr. Glencannon, not to be outdone, promptly fell out of the carriage.

"Heigh-nanny, lass!" said the terrier with the bonnet, swaggering up to Mary and kissing her full upon her luscious black lips without so much as a by-your-leave. "I'm Jock o' the Dumbartons, senior dog o' the reegiment. Welcome to Geebraltar!" Mary stood blushing, eyes downcast but heart throbbing wildly. . . . Mr. Glencannon and Cousin Douglas were slapping each other on the back, saying "Weel, weel, weel, I'll be domned!" and repeating it over and over again.

"Foosh, Cousin Colin, and it's gude to see you!" roared the giant at length. "Why, ye domned old ghoul, ye, when did we meet, the last?"

"Let me think, let me think," said Mr. Glencannon, closing his eyes and grasping the carriage lamp for support. "Why, o' course! —it was Nineteen-fufteen, when I was Second on the transpoort takin' ye oot to Gallipoli."

"Thirteen years ago—eh, to think of it!" sighed Cousin Douglas, and the sigh was as the sound of a locomotive plunging into a tunnel. "Weel,"—and he wrinkled his nose, smacked his lips, and cast his eye on the case of whisky partly concealed by the carriage rug, "Weel, it's customarra in such happy ceercumstances . . ."

"—I was aboot to suggest it!" hastened Mr. Glencannon. "Coachman, I'll thank ye for the loan o' a corkscrew."

"Dinna trouble yersel'," said Cousin Douglas, seizing a bottle and smiting it so lustily against his palm that the cork leapt out as from the choicer vintages of Rheims. "Come, Cousin Colin, do we mount yon carriage the twa o' us, an' go see the bullfight over in Spanish Town. 'Twull be better than the futball. But feerst, let us drink a drap to our happy meeting. Here—I'll open another bottle so we'll both have one." . . . He tilted his own quart beneath his bristly red moustache; and when he took it down again, lo, it was only a pint.

"Haw!" he snorted, closing his eyes ecstatically and holding the bottle at arm's length, " 'Tis the Dew o' Kirkintilloch! I dinna ha' to look at the label—I recognize the way it treeckles doon an' cozeys my sluggish liver! 'Tis a happy meetin', Cousin Colin—a happy meetin' indeed!"

He climbed aboard the carriage, which groaned in every joint and took an alarming list to starboard as he settled into the seat. Mr. Glencannon was about to join him, when he saw Mary and the mascot joyfully gambolling across the troop-filled field.

" 'Tis a-richt, peerfectly a-richt," Cousin Douglas assured him, "Let the little tykes frusk aboot while the lads are playin' futball. I'll tell MacPheerson and MacColquhoun to keep an eye on them, and leave them with Corporal MacClintoch at the Frontier guard house.—Ye see," he explained, "We're off juty today to play the 67th Arteelery—attendance optional. My time's my ain till evening gun. So, carra on, coachman!"

The driver beat several clouds of dust out of the hide of his nag, and headed for the border. At the British side they were halted by a Highlander who blanched perceptibly as he recognized Sergeant Douglas Glencannon.

"I'll thank ye for a look at your passes, gentlemen," he said, saluting.

"Tak' a gude look at this, Corporal MacClintoch!" replied Cousin Douglas, extending a fist the size of a hoof, and quivering it threateningly beneath the guardian's nose. "Tak' a verra gude look, while ye're still alive to see it!"

"Thank ye," said Corporal MacClintoch, backing up a trifle, and saluting again. "Yere passes are sateesfactorra."

They jogged across the Neutral Strip—a stretch of meadow in which the kine of Castile and Britain browsed in sisterly contentment—and paused again, for inspection at the Spanish Customs. The *aduanero* was a fat gentleman in a blue uniform and a sword left over from the American War. "Have you tobacco or spirits?" he asked in perfect English.

"I dinna ken your lingo," replied Cousin Douglas, smacking a fresh bottle against his palm, and watching the cork sail into a roadside cactus. "Drive on, gilly!"

The coachman was plainly troubled. "Tell heem you have no the tobacco, no the alcohol," he whispered.

Without removing his feet from the opposite cushions, Cousin Douglas leaned halfway across the road and seized the *aduanero* by the throat. Dragging him to the side of the carriage he shook him playfully.

"Pass!" gurgled the guard, retreating into his hut and swallowing diligently—"*Vaya con Dios!*" The driver clucked to his horse, and five minutes later they turned into the main street of La Linea de la Concepcion, headed for the bull ring. Evidently, from the cheering, the *corrida* was already in progress.

Arrived at the Plaza, Mr. Glencannon dismounted first. "Do ye please tak' charge o' the refreeshments, Cousin Dooglas, while I pay for the cab," he said, handing the driver a counterfeit Costa Rican *colon* and three brass Chinese coins with holes in them. The Spaniard raised his voice in protest, whereupon Cousin Douglas, standing in the carriage with the case of whisky under his arm, jumped into the air thrice and so mightily that the vehicle broke into two distinct halves. As he stood triumphant in the splintered wreck of the rear section, the terrified horse, the driver and the front wheels vanished in a dust-cloud down the street.

A crowd collected, and through it five cocked-hatted policemen shouldered their way. They took one look at Cousin Douglas, and shouldered their way out again.

Mr. Glencannon placed a shilling on the ledge of the ticket booth. "Twa!" he ordered, holding up two fingers. The Spaniard shook his head and pointed at the scale of prices. "*Dos duros, Senores,*" he said.

"Twa duros!" snorted Cousin Douglas, "Why, 'tis rank extortion! Dinna submeet to it, Cousin Colin, dinna submeet!" Seizing the ticket booth by one of its upper corners, he rocked it back and forth so violently that the Spaniard, the cash-till and two chairs went rattling about the interior like peas in a withered pod. Then, reaching through the window, he seized a sheaf of tickets and led the way through the cool shadowy tunnel which gave access to the seats.

They entered the first vacant box and were about to sit down when the audience burst into a storm of frenzied *"vivas!"* Ortiz, the Seville Sticker, had manoeuvred his bull into a perfect *pase de la firma,* and dispatched him with a masterly thrust. *"Oreja! Oreja!"* screamed the crowd; and at a sign from the President of the *corrida,* a man sliced an ear off the bull and handed it—the highest of honors—to the *matador.*

Ortiz, in his heelless slippers, strutted bowing around the *sombra* side of the arena, amid a shower of hats, fans and flowers.

"Oh!" exclaimed Mr. Glencannon, "Look, Cousin Dooglas—you can throw things! Foosh! what fun!" And falling wholeheartedly into the spirit of it all, he tossed a chair over the barrier and knocked the *matador* flat.

In that instant the cheers turned into the menacing roar of a mob whose idol has been desecrated. Wheeling about, Cousin Douglas saw a thousand Spaniards descending upon them with murder in their eyes. His bottle was almost empty; so hesitating only to empty it completely, he hurled it into the front rank with withering effect. Four chairs were handy, and he flung them with unerring aim. A policeman appeared with drawn sword. Cousin Douglas seized the sword, spanked him with it, and grasped him by the belt and threw him across seven tiers of seats. The seats were vacant—in fact by this time they had an entire section of the arena to themselves.

"Weel," he said, languidly, settling himself beside Mr. Glencannon, who had been busy uncorking bottles, "We can better enjoy the speetacle noo, without the fumes o' garlic from yon feelthy Spaniards."

"Ye're richt," agreed Mr. Glencannon, impatiently viewing the group which bore Ortiz from the arena on a stretcher, "But if they dinna proceed with their domned bull-sticking soon, I shall deemand our money back."

"A verra reasonable and tolerant deecision, Cousin Colin! We're being imposed upon by these swundling foreigners, and it's time we asseerted oursel's!"

Grasping the captured sword, he was about to go out and complain to the management when a fanfare of trumpets gave him pause. A herald appeared upon the bloody sand below.

"Hoot!" applauded Mr. Glencannon, pounding his bottle on the ledge of the box, "He's aboot to eloqute! Lusten closely, Cousin Dooglas!"

Choosing his words according to the conventions of the *Corrida,* the herald announced that El Vaquerito, the thrice-eminent *espada* from Bilbao, would match wits with a bull *"con buenos adornos en la pensadora"*—which meant a most intelligent bull indeed. The bull, he went on to say, was none other than *El Maquinista. . . .*

"L. MacKinister!" exclaimed Mr. Glencannon. "Did ye hear that name, Cousin Dooglas?"

"I canna believe my ears! Why, he must be a MacKinister o' Kirkintilloch! A Scottish bull!"

Mr. Glencannon grasped him by the arm. "Cousin Dooglas," he hissed, "we canna permeet it!"

"Ye're domned richt we canna!" boomed Cousin Douglas, seizing his sword, showing the two remaining bottles into his sporran, and rising to his full seven feet. "Come, Cousin Colin—the Glencannons are gaein' to the wars!"

They vaulted the rail of the box and clambered over the barrier into the arena. Three thousand Spaniards shouted, but only twenty interfered. Cousin Douglas attended to fourteen, and Mr. Glencannon disposed of six. "'Twas dry and theersty work," observed Mr. Glencannon, surveying the scene of carnage.—"Thank ye, Cousin Dooglas—I ha' a bottle o' my ain."

Occupied as they were, neither of them saw El Maquinista as he rushed snorting into the sunlight. Spotting Cousin Douglas's flaming scarlet kilt from afar, he thundered toward it. A mighty shout came from the audience.

"Lusten to them, Cousin Dooglas—why, I do believe they're giving us a cheer!" Mr. Glencannon raised his cap in a graceful gesture of acknowledgment, and Cousin Douglas made a courtly bow. As he did so, El Maquinista's horn very neatly removed his kilt, and left him with nothing below the waist save gaiters, shoes and stockings.

"Oh, shame, shame, Cousin Dooglas!" cried Mr. Glencannon, "Quick, lad—do ye stand in back o' me and pull down your sporran!"

" 'Twull be inadeequate," announced Cousin Douglas. "Look yonder, Collin—that domned bull has trompled my kilt all to nowt!"

A great rage came upon him. Despite Mr. Glencannon's scandalised protests, he strode across the arena and addressed the bewildered bull.

"Ye lout, ye!" he shouted, shaking his fist in the animal's face. "Ye ruddy garlic-eating impostor, ye! Ye're no Scot—ye're a feelthy, treecherous, back-knifing Spaniard, that's what ye are!"

El Maquinista bellowed, put down his head, and charged. Cousin Douglas stood his ground and met the charge with a right to the nose and a left jab to the eye. Stepping in, he landed blow after blow, every one of which jolted the bull from stem to stern.

"I'll knock ye oot, ye big booby, ye!" panted Cousin Douglas. "Another minute, and I'll uncoork the uppercut that made me Champion o' the Breetish Army."

Mr. Glencannon took out his watch, and stood solemnly by, ready to time the count. El Maquinista, both eyes closed and bleeding at the nose, was groggy on his feet when the bullfighters intervened. As they drove the bull out of the arena Cousin Douglas knocked out a couple of *toreros* for good measure. "Quick, Cousin Colin!" he shouted. "Help me borrow their troosers!" Together they had yanked most of the clothing off the limp Spaniards, when they saw five *picadores* galloping toward them, lances couched.

"Run for yere life, Cousin Dooglas—here comes the cavalry!" warned Mr. Glencannon; and dropping most of their spoils, they sprinted for the runway down which El Maquinista had vanished. He was standing just within the entrance, but he hastily stood aside when he recognized Cousin Douglas.

Climbing over the wall of the runway, they plunged into the labyrinthian foundations of the stadium. In the distance, they heard the hue and cry raised after them. Groping on their way, they came to a hole in the wall, and they crawled through it to find themselves in the back yard of a wine-shop.

"Foosh!" said Mr. Glencannon. "What a happy coeencidence! Let us gae in, Cousin Dooglas, and subdue the proprieter."

The *tabernero* was alone among his wine barrels, so Cousin

Douglas imprisoned him within one, and sat upon it. "Oh, deary me, but I've a theerst on me!" he said. "Mak' haste, Cousin Colin, and let us quaff our fill."

"Verra weel," agreed Mr. Glencannon, inspecting the rows of bottles on the shelf, "I canna read any o' them, so we'll ha' to sample them all."

At this point things became curiously garbled. It seemed that a great deal was transpiring over a long period of time, but Mr. Glencannon's next really definite impression was of a splitting headache. He lay with eyes closed, his very soul cringing as white hot twinges of migraine surged through his brain.

Opening his eyes, he found that he was in his own room aboard the *Inchcliffe Castle,* and that he was wearing the green velvet jacket of a Spanish *matador.* Painfully hoisting himself to a sitting posture, he saw Mary Queen of Scots upon the floor, contentedly chewing a bull's ear.

"Bless me, I remember noo!" he chuckled, "Daddy brought it hame to his lass as a souvenir of Spain."

Mary wagged her tail and continued chewing.

"Weel," sighed Mr. Glencannon, lurching to his feet, "I wonder if we've coaled yet. Why! I do believe we're at sea!" He peered through the port at a blue expanse of Mediterranean across which trailed a long black smudge from the *Inchcliffe Castle's* funnel. He opened the port and gratefully gulped down the fresh, cool breeze. In the corner of his room were piled the five new cases of the Dew of Kirkintilloch, and uncorking a bottle, he poured himself a brimming tumblerful.

"Thur's no cure for dog-bite like the hair of the dog that bit ye!" he remarked to Mary, tossing it off and smacking his lips. Then, donning his working clothes, he made his way to the engine room —head clear, step brisk, and hand steady.

"Strike me ruddy, but the Chief's a wonder!" observed Mr. Swales, the Second Mate. "To look at 'im, this arfternoon, you'd think 'e was the H'Archbishop of Canterb'ry!"

"'Is recuperating powers are remarkable," agreed Mr. Montgomery. "I 'ad 'Ell's own time gettin' 'im out of the tender larst night. There was 'im and another wild man—a non-com. 'Igh-lander nine foot tall, with nothing on below the wyste but one of

them 'airy Scotch tobacco pouches, like. Singin' '*Scots wha hae wi'*
Wallace bled,' they were, and drinking out of bottles. They 'ad
another of them black tykes with 'em, syme as Mary—wearing a
little Scotch bonnet, 'e was."

"Well, the Scotch are a mad race," said Mr. Swales.

"Mad as 'Ell," agreed Mr. Montgomery. "And Mr. Glencannon's
the maddest of the lot. But despite 'is quart a day, not counting
'olidays, he's a great engineer, Mr. Swales, a great engineer."

Some weeks later, though (they had called at Naples, gone to
Cattaro, thence to Odessa, and were westward bound in the Sea
of Candia) Mr. Glencannon's madness took a disquieting form.
He became preoccupied, morose. He spent long hours in his room
with Mary. His appetite dwindled.

At first there was only a rumor. Then the rumor spread
throughout the ship's company until it was discussed incredulously from fo'c'sle to engine room. *Mr. Glencannon had sworn off
liquor!*

"The thing is serious," declared Captain Ball, shaking his head
ominously. "A man who has drank all his life like Mr. Glencannon
has drank, can't shut down on it all at once."

" 'E can't indeed!" said Mr. Montgomery. "But are you sure 'e
'as really sworn orff, Sir!"

"Yes. Last night I asked him if he'd lend me the loan of a little
whisky to rub on my corns. He said 'Take all I've got and welcome, Captain—I'm quit o' the feelthy stuff!' "

"H'm," mused the Mate. "That looks bad, Sir.—Specially, offering you all 'e's got, 'im being of the Scottish persuasion, as you
might say."

"Exactly! And he went moping off to his room saying he had to
fix some medicine for Mary. She's sick or something, too."

"Sick my aunt, Sir! It's only the way 'e pampers the poor tyke!
Meanwhile, 'e's letting 'is engines go to 'Ell."

"H'm. I noticed we were quite a bit shy on yesterday's run."

In the engine room things went from bad to worse. The Assistant Engineers, though diligently they slaved, lacked the great
genius of their Chief which could make the old coffee grinder
behave like clock work.

South of Kapsali they ran into dirty weather, and the poor old

Castle took a sorry buffeting. She went rails under every roll, and the forward well-deck was a surge of green water.

Captain Ball, a notorious coal saver, had laid his course close. They were less than a mile off the thundering white breakers, when the engines sighed, wheezed, and stopped. From the gratings and ventilators came clouds of steam, and the sound of hammers and scurrying feet. Mr. Montgomery leaped to the speaking tube, and addressed the engine room. "'Urry up, you bleddy tinkers!" he screamed. "If you don't get way on 'er smartly you'll swim out through the condenser pipes!"

Captain Ball then stepped to the tube, and said a few words of his own. Those nearby could smell the rubber gums of his false teeth burning. When he had finished, he went alone into the starboard wing of the bridge and considered the situation. Things were bad—very bad. In an hour, at most, they would pile up on a lee shore. He started toward his room to gather the ship's log, his Bible, chronometers and hair tonic preparatory to ordering away the boats. Half down the ladder he was blinded by a stinging gust of spray, and as he groped on his way he encountered some one coming up.

"Hoot, Captain!" shouted Mr. Glencannon, grasping his superior officer in a joyous and drunken embrace. "I was just gaein' up to get you! Stup into my room a moment, Sir—stup into my room!"

"Hell's bones, not now!" gasped the Captain, as he dragged Mr. Glencannon into the lee of the house. "We're due to pile up any minute, man! Can't you feel that the engines are stopped?"

"I was aboot to mak' appropreeate comment on the fact," said Mr. Glencannon, feigning a polite interest. "But if you'll just come wi' me a moment, Captain, and stup into my room, I'll go below in pairson and repair them. It reminds me of a story I once heard aboot a . . ."

In desperation Captain Ball led the way across the rolling deck to Mr. Glencannon's room, and threw open the door.

"There, Captain," said the Engineer proudly, indicating the bunk with one hand and seizing a bottle with the other. "Look what the Angels ha' brought Mary and her puir old Dad!"

On the center of the bed lay Mary Queen of Scots, feebly wagging her tail, and caressing six tiny squirming black shapes with a tender maternal muzzle.

"The reesponsibility—Ah, the reesponsibility's been terrible, Captain! But noo I'm my ain old self again. Do ye mak' yersel' comfortable for half a moment, Sir, while I just stup below and start those engines."

Weak and trembling, Captain Ball settled in a chair. This, he thought, would be as good a place to die as any. For the first time in his life he felt his years, and the tragic grief of a master about to lose his ship. Smiling bitterly, he patted Mary's hot little head. She raised it from her puppies and gratefully licked his hand. And at this instant there commenced a rhythmic throbbing underfoot! The *Inchcliffe Castle* became alive again! Mr. Glencannon, the wizard of steam, had worked a miracle with the engines!

Captain Ball arose slowly to his feet. Yes, the *Inchcliffe Castle* was ploughing along on her course. "Thank God—and three rousing cheers for Scotland!" he said.

In less than an hour, the *Castle* was around the Cape and in calm waters. Mr. Glencannon, oily, happy and thirsty, came back to his room.

"Weel, Lass!" he said, picking up the bottle, "I see that the Captain has gone. And—why, the domned old teetotal hypocrite! Look, Mary—he drank up half a pint o' Papa's Dew o' Kirkintilloch!"

NONSENSE!

⌇ᴣ JACK GOODMAN
⌇ᴣ ALBERT RICE

J. P. McEvoy, it will be conceded, knows a good story when he sees one. In a magazine article, he re-tells this one—attributed to Ed Wynn—and warns the reader that the imagination must supply Wynn's futile, fluttering gestures, silly lisp, and infectious giggle.

A sleight-of-hand artist was going great guns in his performance during a ship's concert. The audience was delightfully mystified, and a curious and somewhat surprised parrot was teetering on a perch overlooking the scene.

With a few deft passes, the performer made an entire deck of cards disappear. The audience applauded vigorously and the parrot cocked his head to one side and blinked.

The magician then made a goldfish bowl, a tablecloth, and several assorted odds and ends disappear in quick succession. The parrot forgot the teeter and watched it all in silence.

Then the magician said: "And now, my friends, I will show you a feat unparalleled in the history of legerdemain!"

Just as the last syllables were ringing through the room, there was a tremendous explosion. Lights went out, whistles blew, bells rang. The audience dispersed in panic—and the ship sank.

A little later we find the parrot sitting on a piece of driftwood. He saw the magician come up to the surface, shout "Help!" and go down. Again the man came up, again he yelled "Help!", again he disappeared. The third time he went down for good. Now there was no trace of boat, passengers or performer. The parrot thought about it for a while and then softly murmured: "Amazing!"

Which is the identical reaction set up in most of us, after we've stopped chuckling, by really good nonsense. There is a lot of it around nowadays, since the retort ridiculous is probably the most widely used of all forms of repartee. Robert Benchley, Donald Ogden Stewart, James Thurber, Frank Sullivan, S. J. Perelman, and dozens of others are mainly nonsensical in tone.

Nonsense repartee, first class, is a seemingly insane but actually brilliant combination of the rational and the irrational. Careening from a logical beginning to a topsy-turvy conclusion, it completely surprises, not only listeners, but sometimes its authors as well. It lurches into practically all categories of humor, even those outlined in this book. It can be a Betterism, insanely drunk—a lunatic Far Fetch, or a wild-eyed pun. Because its shock content is generally greater than most other types, it produces more spontaneous guffawing than any of the others.

It can be utterly harmless and directed at no one, as Groucho Marx, one of its major prophets, is continually proving. The general technique is illustrated in a passage from the Kaufman–Ryskind *Animal Crackers*—in which Groucho recounts his experiences as an explorer in something like this vein:

"The first day saw us begin an active life—up at six—then breakfast—then back in bed by seven" . . . and again: "One night I shot an elephant in my pajamas. How he got in my pajamas I don't know."

Nonsense wit, however, is capable of as pretty savagery as any other type. D. B. Wyndham Lewis's little fantasy about Aesop not only affords a chuckle, but speaks for masses of dumb fauna at the same time. It goes, roughly, like this: Aesop was walking through a forest when a wolf came up and bit him savagely.

"Now go home and write that up," said the wolf pleasantly.

A specialty of Ring Lardner's was the choice of normal words in nonsensical situations to produce brilliant effects. His description of a baseball player soars into greatness through the use of one ordinary word:

"Although he is a bad fielder," he wrote, "he is also a very poor hitter."

And if you think that *although* in that sentence was the choice of genius, consider the use of the last word in the following passage from *The Young Immigrunts:*

The lease said about I and my fathers trip from The Bureau of Manhattan to our new home the soonest mended. In some way either he or I got balled up on the grand concorpse and next thing you know we was threatening to swoop down on Pittsfield.

"Are you lost Daddy?" I asked tenderly.

"Shut up," he explained.

Under the nonsense treatment, the most logical of beginnings will mushroom into weird conclusions, as in another Marxist fancy —Groucho's discussion with Chico of the advisability of building a house near the railroad track. A worried look appears above Groucho's mustache. He says: "I don't like Junior to cross the tracks on his way to the reform school."

Which is obvious enough humor, and would remain unsung by these commentators—were it not for the fact that Groucho has not quite finished. "In fact," he continues thoughtfully, "I don't like Junior."

The thoughtfully mad expansion of a commonplace idea was also handled effectively by the gentleman viewing the Parthenon ruins: "What a story these old walls would tell," he said reverently, "if I would only listen."

Then there seems to be an entirely reverse brand, which, for want of a better name, we might call the nonsensical sequitur. This sort generally contains much more satire, viciousness, or plain debunking than other kinds of nonsense. It is accomplished by an insane adherence to the literal. Bion, an ancient Greek who has been conceded by scholars to be the first master of the wise-crack, set the pattern when he said to a sorrowing lover, "Don't tear your hair out—baldness is no cure for sorrow."

Some time later, Robert Benchley used the same device in a review: "I used to say that I would laugh at Phil Baker and Lou Holtz until the cows came home. Well—the cows came home last Thursday night."

Which inevitably brings to mind that oft-told story of Mr. Benchley and the girl Nubi, another example of the stunning blows which may be dealt with a jester's wand. It was the first night of a very tropical play, and Nubi was the name of the tropical lass. A point in the drama was reached in which Nubi sidled up to a messy-looking white man and drawled: "Me Nubi. Nubi like white man. Nubi stay."

It took the better part of half a second for Mr. Benchley to slip into the aisle, mutter "Me Robert Benchley. Robert Benchley no like play. Robert Benchley go."—and beat a hasty exit.

Without personal sting, but equally sardonic, was the little excerpt reprinted from a speech by Judge Kelly of Chicago in Ed Sullivan's column a few months back. The clipping has been lost, but the general idea is engraved upon your correspondents' memory.

"My friends," said the jurist earnestly, "money is not all. It is not money that will mend a broken heart or reassemble the fragments of a dream. Money cannot brighten the hearth nor repair the portals of a shattered home." He paused, then concluded solemnly, "I refer, of course, to Confederate money."

Identical in wryness is the comment attributed to Damon Runyon: "It may be that the race is not always to the swift, nor the battle to the strong . . . but that's the way to bet."

The nonsensical sequitur can also be pure nonsense without any malicious content. Harry Ruby and Bert Kalmar have dashed off several speciments of this type, excellent ones such as those spoken by Groucho, again—in *Monkey Business:*

"There's a man outside with a black mustache," says his secretary.

"Tell him I've got one," says Groucho.

THE DEAF ADDER

◆§ COLIN HOWARD

Readers who remember Marcus, my huge, handsome, lazy, stupid St. Bernard, may be interested and incredulous to know that he recently had an idea.

Ideas are not things that come readily to St. Bernards. Their heads are not built for ideas. They bear a strong resemblance to that prehistoric monster that employed its head solely as a battering-ram, and kept its brains in its tail. Only of course a St. Bernard's tail is very little more intelligent than its head. This idea was certainly the first idea Marcus ever had in his life. I cannot think how he recognized it.

The idea had to do with the easing of life for St. Bernards. For some time past Marcus had been growing steadily more disgruntled with life. It is his belief that life should consist of sixteen hours of sleep, six hours of rest, and two hours of intensive eating. His only hobby is chasing cats, which he either loathes or considers edible—I am not sure which. However, the local cats do not suffer much. It will be seen that Marcus's day does not leave much time for cat-chasing.

But—and here lies the root of Marcus's moody dissatisfaction with life—he is occasionally called on to work. His work comprises a sullen amble after breakfast as far as the nearest corner and back. A real dog would look forward to this walk for hours beforehand, trembling with expectation. To Marcus it is sheer, brutal slavery.

Roughly, then, his idea was this: "If I were deaf I couldn't hear them when they called me for my walk, and they wouldn't be able to shift me, because nothing can shift me. So I will pretend to be deaf."

I do not claim Marcus thought it all out as neatly and briskly as that. He must have spent a good many weeks working out the advantages of deafness, and several more gloomily repining because he wasn't deaf. That he should pretend deafness was a flash of inspiration that probably seeped into his enormous head in a matter of days.

After all this thinking, Marcus presumably spent a month or two quietly recuperating under the kitchen table. The floor under the kitchen table is his favorite day-bed because he honestly believes he cannot be seen there, and therefore cannot be made to work. On the rare occasions that he rises, the table rises too. Highly-strung visitors, faced with his frightening apparition, have been known to go away and tell people we keep a howdah'd elephant in the kitchen.

At last he put his plan into execution. My wife came to me, much perturbed.

"Poor old Marcus has gone deaf!" she exclaimed.

"Deaf?" I cried. "But he could hear perfectly well last night."

"Well, he can't hear a thing now. Come and speak to him."

I came into the kitchen and addressed Marcus. Into his mournful eyes came the glazed expression of one who is jolly well not going to hear. I ought to have understood immediately; but who would credit a St. Bernard with having an idea?

"Poor old lad!" I said. "Perhaps it'll pass off. Coming for a walk, Marcus?"

Marcus, with masterly histrionism, gazed at me with eager devotion, as though he would have given his last bone to have heard what I said.

After a good deal of persuasive shouting we left him where he was, and he went to sleep smiling.

It was some days before we noticed Marcus was only partially deaf. He was still able to hear anything connected with food, such as a plate set on the floor to be licked, or a courteously-worded announcement that his supper was served. We went on talking to him about food and not talking to him about anything else. While this lasted he was the happiest St. Bernard in Great Britain. He wouldn't have changed with Rip van Winkle. But we realized a certain inconsistency about his deafness one Sunday when I was carving the joint. A tiny scrap of meat slipped from the fork and dropped on to the carpet. The dining-room is one room and a passage away from the kitchen, where Marcus, tired after his rest, was asleep, but he heard it fall. A blurred, tawny avalanche hurtled out of the kitchen and into the dining-room, and had wolfed the scrap almost before it had landed.

"Hey!" I said. "I thought you were deaf?"

Marcus's jaw and tail both dropped. He went back into character immediately, but the seeds of suspicion were sown. He lay down to rest—it is, as I have said, a long way from the kitchen to the dining-room—and to try to work out some logical means by which he could still hear anything to do with food but could remain deaf to all else.

He failed to find an answer, so he did without one. He continued to hear on one subject only. My wife, who is the most charitable person alive, and a constant film-goer, at first attributed this to schizophrenia. When we had finished arguing about the pronunciation, she went on to assert that this proved what she had always maintained—that Marcus had a mind somewhere. If he hadn't, she said, how could it be split? She wanted me to psychoanalyze him.

But even my wife grew suspicious of the selectivity of Marcus's hearing when, in one short hour, he failed to hear three commands to come out for a walk, one bellow to put that milk-bottle down at once, a number of hysterical appeals to get out of her way for goodness' sake and let her get at the stove, and a stern lecture on the sanctity of the bread-board; but heard without difficulty a cat in the next road, the arrival of the butcher, and an invitation to finish a pot of fish-paste that had gone off.

When she was convinced of his guile she agreed with me he had to be cured. But how? The course we took was not, perhaps, entirely sporting. Marcus had gone deaf, *we* went silent.

When Marcus was around, we went through all the actions and expressions of speaking without uttering a word. Marcus began by being lazily puzzled. Very soon he was really worried. Had he overestimated his will-power and gone *really* deaf?

The horrible part of course was that, for all he knew, we might be talking food all day long, discussing dainties we had put out in the garden for Marcus, asking him if he fancied a few biscuits?

The thought of what he might be missing was torture to him. He would lie staring agonizedly into our faces as we mouthed silently at one another—trying, I will swear, to lip-read.

As he never got called for meals, he had to look out for them himself, and he hardly dared close his eyes in case he missed one. I doubt if he got fourteen hours' real sleep out of the twenty-four, and he worried himself down to about three hundredweight.

We kept it up for a few days. Then we decided to restore Marcus's hearing to him. I said aloud: "Come on, Marcus! Time for your walk, boy!"

An expression of beautiful relief spread over his vast face, taking about one minute to do so. He wasn't deaf after all. He bounded to his feet. He frisked to the gate like a mettlesome carthorse. He joyously took one of the longest walks of his career—almost half a mile.

Heavens, how he slept that week!

He was not troubled again with his deafness. Neither were we.

THE BIRTHDAY PARTY

⌁ EVAN HUNTER

He was still very intoxicated when the pilot or the purser, or whoever it was, made the announcement. His head rolled over to one side, and he gazed through the window just level with his right shoulder, and down to the ground below where he could see beginning pinpoints of light in the distance. He was wondering what it was the loudspeaker had announced, when a blonde stewardess came up the aisle and paused and smiled. "Would you please fasten your seat belt, sir?" she asked.

"I would be happy to," he answered. He smiled back at her, and then began looking for the seat belt, lifting his behind and reaching under him to pull it free, and then fumbling very hard to fasten it, while the blonde stewardess stood patiently smiling in the aisle.

"May I help you, sir?" she asked.

"Please," he said.

She ducked her head a little as she moved toward him past the empty aisle seat. Smiling, standing balanced just a bit to his left, she caught up both ends of the seat belt and was clasping them together when he lightly and impishly ran his right hand up the inside of her leg. She did not jump or scream or anything. She just continued fastening the seat belt, with the smile still on her face, and then she backed away into the aisle again, saying, "There you are, sir."

He was enormously surprised. He thought Now that is poise, that is what I really call poise, and then he wondered whether there possibly hadn't been a short-circuit from his brain to his hand, causing the brain-command to be issued but not executed. In which case, nothing at all had happened and the girl's tremendously impressive icy poise and aloofness, her ability to remain a staid and comforting mother-image in the face of danger was really nothing to marvel at, boy am I drunk, he thought.

He could not imagine how he had got so drunk since he absolutely knew for a concrete fact that it was an ironbound rule of airplane companies the world over never to serve any of its passengers more than two drinks of whiskey. He suspected, however, that he had been drinking a stupefying amount of booze long before he'd boarded the plane, though he couldn't quite remember all of it too clearly at the moment, especially since everything seemed to begin spinning all at once, the lights below springing up to his window in startling red and green and white proximity, oh mother, we are going to crash, he thought.

He recognized at once, and to his enormous relief, that the plane was only banking for a turn on its approach to an airport, probably New York though he could not remember ever seeing lights like those on the approach to New York, scattered for miles, spilled brokenly across the landscape, oh that was a beautiful sight down there, he wished he knew where the hell he was.

The poised young blonde stewardess opened the folding door between sections, and then walked briskly forward again, preparatory to taking her own seat and fastening her own belt. She was carrying a blanket or something, they always seemed to be tidying up an airplane just before it landed. He said, "Miss?" and when she stopped he noticed that she kept her distance. "Miss, where are we? We're coming down someplace, aren't we?"

"Yes?"

"Well, *where* are we coming down?" he asked.

"Los Angeles," she said.

"Oh, good," he answered. "I've never been to Los Angeles before." He paused, and then smiled. "Miss?"

"Yes, what is it? I've got to take a seat."

"I know. I just wanted to ask you something. Did I put my hand under your skirt?"

"Yes, you did."

"Just a little while ago?"

"Yes."

"Thank you," he said.

"Is that all?"

"Yes, thank you."

The stewardess smiled. "All right," she said. She started up the aisle again, stopped, turned back, leaned over, and whispered, "Your hands are cold."

"Thank you," he said.

"All right," she answered, and smiled, and left.

He pressed his forehead to the glass and watched the lights drawing closer and closer. He could see moving automobiles below now, and neon signs, and traffic signals blinking on and off, the Lionel train set his father had bought him for Christmas long ago, toy houses puffing smoke, reach down like God and lift the little automobiles, the movie with Roland Young where the huge pointing finger of God came down over his head. There was speed suddenly, a sense of blinding speed as the ground moved up and the airport buildings flashed by in a dizzying blur. He felt the vibration of the wheels when they touched.

He thought it's all over.

"We have just landed at Los Angeles International Airport," a voice said. He knew for sure it wasn't the pilot this time, unless they allowed women to fly jet aircrafts, aircraft. "The local time is six forty-five P.M., and the temperature is seventy-eight degrees. May we ask you to please remain seated until we have taxied to the terminal building and our engines have stopped? It has been our pleasure to serve you, and we hope you will be flying with us again in the near future. Thank you, and Merry Christmas."

"Thank *you*," he said aloud, "and a Merry Christmas to you, too." He immediately unfastened his seat belt and rose to take his coat from the rack overhead. The stewardess' voice came over the loudspeaker in gentle warning. "Ladies and gentlemen, *please* remain seated until the aircraft has taxied to a stop. Thank you."

"Thank you," he said again, "you forgot to say Merry Christmas." He did not bother to sit because he figured the aircraft must surely have taxied to a stop by now, although he could still hear engines. He was putting on his coat when the blonde stewardess came up the aisle to him. "Sir," she said, "would you please remain seated until we have taxied and stopped?"

"Certainly," he said, but he did not sit.

"Sir, we'd appreciate it . . ."

"You are the most poised young lady I ever met in my life," he said.

"Thank you, but . . ."

"Are you Swedish?"

"No, sir, I . . ."

"We have a girl in our office from Sweden, she's very poised, too. At the Christmas party today, she jumped off the window."

"She *what?*" the stewardess said. "She jumped out the window?"

"No. Of course not! She jumped *off* the window. *Off* it. The sill."

"Oh," the stewardess said.

"What's your name?" he asked her.

"Miss Radley."

"That doesn't sound Swedish at all," he said. "*My* name is Arthur. Everyone calls me Doc."

"Are you a doctor?"

"No, I'm an art director, but everyone calls me Doc. *What* did
you say your name was?"

"Miss Radley. Iris Radley."

"Boy, that is some funny name for a Swedish girl," he said.

"Why do they call you Doc?" she asked.

"Because I wear eyeglasses."

"Well, Doc," she said, "you've successfully remained standing
all the whole while we taxied."

"Thank you," he said.

"Have a nice time in Los Angeles."

"I will. I've never been here before."

"It's a nice city."

"I'm sure it's a beautiful city. It has beautiful lights."

"Do you know where the baggage area is?" she asked, concerned. They were walking forward now, toward the exit. His
overcoat felt very bulky all at once.

"No," he said, "where *is* the baggage area?"

"Have you got your claim tickets?"

"No," he said.

"Oh, dear, did you lose them?"

"No. As a matter of fact, I don't *have* any baggage. I'm traveling light. Well," he said, turning to the exit and peering through it
down the steps and beyond to the terminal building, "Los Angeles." He extended his hand. "Goodbye, Miss Radley, and Merry
Christmas."

"Merry Christmas," she said.

He went down the steps.

He knew at once that he had done the right thing. The air was
balmy, it touched his cheeks, it kissed his face, it riffled his hair.
He took off his coat, oh, he had done the right thing, he had most
certainly done the right thing, though it was unimaginable to even
imagine having done the wrong thing after so many drinks and
kissing Trudy in MacLeish's darkened office. It was impossible to
imagine having made the wrong decision, not after feting old Mr.
Benjamin of Benjamin Luggage, and racing out of the building
with whoever the hell those girls were from Accounting, her hand
so warm and moist in his pocket, the air crisp, church bells bonging, bonging someplace, Salvation Army virgins playing horns and

drums. Oh what a city at Christmas, what a New York, how could anything be wrong, everything *had* to be right, right, right. They talked an off-duty cab driver into taking them out to Kennedy Airport. The cabbie was anxious to get home, "too much goddamn traffic in this goddamn city," but he slipped him a fin even before they opened the door, and suddenly there was no more traffic in the city, suddenly everything was Christmas Eve again and church bells were bonging joy to the world.

Long Island was where Kennedy International Airport was, you had to remember not to call it Idlewild anymore because that would automatically date you as being forty-one years old, that was very bad, going on forty-two imminently. Trudy was nineteen, she wore candy-striped stockings and a short suede skirt, and he had kissed her in MacLeish's office. She had said, "Why, Mr. Pitt, how nasty," but he had kept right on kissing her, and she, too, back. The girls from Accounting, and Arthur, and Benjamin had made the plane in plenty of time, the cabbie was that anxious to show his Christmas spirit after the five-spot tip, had to get old Benjamin Baggage, excuse *me*, Benjamin Luggage, onto that Chicago plane or else Lake Michigan would drift out to sea or something. They stole a plaque from one of the airline counters, it said, "Mr. Schultz," and they gave it to Benjamin as a keepsake. The Chicago plane took off in a roar of screaming jets. Arthur and the two girls from Accounting stood on the observation deck and watched as it soared almost vertically into the sky and then vanished into the clouds. He had an arm around each girl. They were all very drunk, and the girls sighed when the plane disappeared.

"Tomorrow is my birthday," he said to the redhead.

"Happy birthday," she said.

"I only get one present," Arthur said, "because they fall on the same day. My birthday and Christmas. I mean, I get a *lot* of presents, but only *once*. We only celebrate *once*, do you know what I mean?"

"No, I don't," the redhead said, "but you're very cute. Do you know what he means, Phyllis?"

Phyllis said, "No, I don't know what he means, gee I miss Mr. Benjamin."

"Listen, I have an idea," Arthur said. "Let's go to Chicago."

"Why not?" the redhead said.

"Listen, what's your name?" he asked.

"Rose."

"Rose, let's you and me and Phyllis here go to Chicago and surprise Mr. Benjamin, what do you say?"

"Okay, why not?" Rose said. "But first let's have another drink."

"Boy, will he be surprised," Phyllis said, and giggled.

"Okay, so let's go," Arthur said, but he knew even then they would not go to Chicago. He knew at once that they would all have another drink, and then the girls would start reconsidering and remembering that it was Christmas Eve and they should be getting home to family and dear ones, and after all Benjamin wasn't expecting them, and did anyone even know where he lived, and how long would it take them to get to Chicago, and all rationalizing crap that people always came up with when something exciting or adventurous was proposed. He knew they would back out, and he wasn't at all surprised when they asked him to get a taxi for them.

Well, tomorrow is my birthday, he thought, standing just outside the terminal building and watching their taxi move into the distance. Well, happy birthday old Doc, time to go home to the family and dear ones, the loved ones, time to go home. Nobody ever wants to go anywhere anymore, boy, what a bunch of party poops. He looked at his watch, but couldn't read the gold numerals on the dial because it was late afternoon, with that curiously flat winter light that causes whites to become whiter and gold to blend indefinably into them, and besides he was drunk. He went back into the terminal to look at the big clock over the counter, and he saw that it was twenty minutes to four, well what the hell, he thought, home James, home to Merry Christmas and such, boy, nobody ever wants to *go* anywhere anymore, boy, what a drag. He heard them calling a flight, and he walked over to the counter and said, "Excuse me, Captain, but what flight was that you just called?"

"The four o'clock flight to Los Angeles," the captain answered, though Arthur knew he wasn't a captain at all, he was just making him feel good.

"I've never been to Los Angeles," he said.

"No?" the captain answered politely.

"No. How much does it cost?"

"How much does what cost?"

"A ticket to Los Angeles, that's the city of Angels, did you know that?"

"That's right, so it is. First-class, sir?"

"First-class, of course."

"First-class round trip to Los Angeles is three twenty-one eighty. Plus tax."

"How much is the tax?"

"Sixteen-oh-nine, sir."

"That sounds very reasonable. Will you take a check?"

"Sir?"

"For the flight you just called. I have identification, if that's what's troubling you."

"No, sir, it's just . . . I don't even know if there's room on that flight, sir. Christmas is our busiest . . ."

"I don't need a room, just a seat." Heh-heh, he thought, how'd you like *that* one, Sonny?

"Well, I'd have to . . ."

"Yes, well go ahead and do it. You said it leaves at four, didn't you?"

"Are you *serious*, sir? Do you really want me to . . . ?"

"Certainly, I'm serious. Of *course*, I'm serious. Nobody the hell *goes* anyplace anymore!"

He knew he would not go through with it, he was just having a little fun with the captain, what the hell tomorrow was his birthday. He knew he would not do it because old Arthur Doc Pitt simply didn't do things like that, flying away from home and hearth on Christmas Eve, what would Jenny say? Jenny would take a fit, that's what Jenny would say. And besides, this really had nothing whatever to do with Jenny or anyone else. It had only to do with old Doc Pitt, who knew he could never never never do something like this, the same way he could not that time in Buffalo when the man sitting in the lobby had asked him if he would like to spend the night with a burlesque queen, or was it even a burlesque queen, *that* part may have been just imagination. In any case, he could not do it then, and he would not do it now, but there was no harm in having a little fun with the good captain here, hanging up the phone now, and putting on a bright smiling cheerful airlines face.

"Well, you certainly are lucky, sir," he said. "There've been some cancellations in the first-class section."

Yeah, well I was only kidding, Arthur thought.

Something started inside him. He knew it was the alcohol, he knew he had had absolutely too much to drink. He knew it was kissing Trudy in MacLeish's office and putting his hand under the short suede skirt, the candy-striped stockings, he knew it was that, nineteen years old, Trudy. He knew it was the wild ride to the airport with the two girls from Accounting, and the soaring disappearance of Benjamin's plane into the clouds, the sudden desperate knowledge that the party was going to end without ever having begun. He knew it was all that, but he suspected it was something more as well, and so he allowed the excitement to grow inside him, teasing himself, saying to himself Go ahead, do it, go ahead, why don't you? and then soberly regarding himself through his eyeglasses, Don't be ridiculous, and then looking at the captain's expectant face and thinking the thing to do was reach into his pocket and slap his check book on the counter and write that goddamn check, he had always wanted to do things like that. The captain was waiting, and the excitement was rising inside Arthur, something that started down in his groin for which he blamed Trudy in MacLeish's office, and climbing up into his chest and his throat and then suddenly leaping into his fingertips which positively twitched with the need to reach into his pocket and slap his check book onto the countertop, You like that Rolls-Royce, kid? It's yours.

The captain was waiting.

"Okay," Arthur said, and reached into his pocket and slapped his check book onto the counter.

"Where to, Mac?"
"A good hotel," he said.
"Lots of good hotels in Los Angeles."
"Like what?"

"You want the city, or Beverly Hills, or what?"

"Beverly Hills," he said. "Why not?"

"Which one in Beverly Hills?"

"The best one."

"They're all good."

"There is only one best one."

The cab driver set the car in motion. "You want the Beverly Hills?"

"I already told you I wanted the Beverly Hills."

"I meant the Beverly Hills *Hotel*."

"Okay, why not?"

"You in the movie racket?"

"No, I am in the advertising game," he said.

"What do you advertise?"

"Benjamin Luggage," he said. "Among other fine products."

"Never heard of it."

"Well, I never heard of the Beverly Hills Hotel," he said.

"They're crying," the cab driver answered, and stepped on the gas.

"This looks like Long Island," Arthur said.

"It ain't," the cabbie replied.

"It sure looks like it. What are all these hot dog stands for? What do you do out here, eat hot dogs all the time?"

"That's right, we eat hot dogs all the time," the cabbie said.

"That's what I thought," Arthur answered. "Boy, what a city. It looks like Long Island. I've never been to Los Angeles."

"That's a shame," the cabbie answered.

"All you do out here is frolic, huh?" he said.

"Yeah, that's all we do out here," the cabbie said.

"What's this we're on now?"

"The San Diego Freeway, heading north."

"Is that where Beverly Hills is?"

"North, right. You been drinking a little bit?" the cabbie asked, which Arthur thought was very clever.

"Yes, a little bit. I have been drinking since twelve o'clock noon New York time."

"That means you've been drinking since nine o'clock this morning, California time."

"That's very clever," Arthur said. "What time is it in London?"

"Who the hell knows?"

"It's seven A.M. Christmas morning," Arthur said, not having the faintest idea what time it was in London or even Bangkok.

"Well, Merry Christmas," the cabbie said, and again lapsed into silence.

"What is this Beverly Hills Hotel?" Arthur asked. "Some kind of fancy hotel, is that what it is?"

"That's what it is."

"In that case, you'd better take me back to the airport," he said.

"What?"

"The airport, the Los Angeles International Airport where it is now six forty-five California time and the temperature is seventy-eight degrees."

"What?"

"You must think I'm crazy or something," he said, "coming all the way out to Los Angeles on Christmas Eve when my wife and family are waiting at home for me."

"Mister, you're not crazy," the cabbie said, "you're drunk."

"You *bet* I am," Arthur said. "I was only kidding, so what the hell am I doing here in Los Angeles?"

"Mister, I don't know. Sometimes I wonder what the hell *I'm* doing here in Los Angeles."

"Well, I don't want to go to the Beverly Hills Hotel," he said.

"Okay, so where *do* you want to go?"

"I don't know."

"You know what my mother told me? My mother told me never pick up no drunks, son, because they will give you grey hairs and a hernia. I'm a working man, mister, I've got a wife and kids waiting home for me, too, this is Christmas Eve. I'd like to get a few calls in and then go home to trim the tree, okay? So where shall it be? The Beverly Hills, the airport, downtown Los Angeles, name it."

"Where's the Beverly Hills?"

"On Sunset Boulevard."

"No, sir," Arthur said. "Absolutely not a hotel on Sunset Boulevard. I saw that movie." He shook his head. "Why don't you take me to the airport where I *want* to go?"

"Okay, I'll get out at the next exit and swing around."

"Are you going to take me to the airport?"

"That's where you want to go, that's where I'll take you."

"Chicken!" Arthur said.

"What?"

"I said you are chicken."

"Now, look, mister, drunk or not . . ."

"Running home to trim your goddam tree!"

"Mister . . ."

"Take me to a hotel, stop arguing."

"Mister . . ."

"Aren't there any hotels except on Sunset Boulevard? You think I came out here to drown face down in a swimming pool?"

"You want the Hilton, mister?" the cabbie said, sighing.

"*What* Hilton?"

"The Beverly Hilton."

"That's very clever," Arthur said. "The Beverly Hilton. I'll bet my bottom dollar it's in Beverly Hills, am I right?"

"You're absolutely right."

"Boy, that's clever," Arthur said. "You people out here are certainly clever."

"That's because we eat so many hot dogs," the cabbie said.

"Yes, and witty, too. Well, do you know what I want you to do? I want you to turn off this highway, thruway, freeway, *whatever* you call it out here, and stop at the *first* hotel you see. The very first hotel you see, *that's* where I want to go. Impromptu," Arthur said. "Im*promp*tu."

"Boy, pick up drunks," the cabbie said.

He felt refreshed and sober when he came out of the shower. There were at least eight mirrors in the bathroom, but he couldn't see himself in any of them because he had taken off his glasses before climbing into the tub. Besides, the bathroom was all steamed up from the hot water he had used, this was certainly a fine hotel with lots of mirrors and good hot water to sober up a wandering soul on Christmas Eve.

I'd better call Jenny, he thought.

He put on his glasses, and picked up his watch. It was still set with New York time, he hadn't bothered to reset it when he got off the plane. In New York, in White Plains to be exact—which is where he and Jenny and Michael and Pam lived, the four little Pitts in a white clapboard house on Robin Hood Lane—it was now eleven P.M., one hour to Christmas, and Jenny was probably frantic. Naked, he put on his watch, and walked out of the bathroom. He found a white ivory telephone on the night table near his bed, wondered whether he should call her or not, and then decided of *course* he had to call her.

He felt chilly all at once. He went to the closet where the bellhop had hung his cashmere overcoat and, lacking a bathrobe or any other boudoir attire, put on the overcoat. The lining was silk. The coat felt luxurious and comforting. He sat on the edge of the bed and crossed his legs and looked at the phone and then became absorbed in reading the dial which listed all the various places you could call in the hotel. There was a little red light on the telephone, too, and he supposed you used that if you wanted a direct line to a red light district, which he might very well want before this night was through. In the meantime, he had to call Jenny so that she wouldn't alert the police or call the hospitals or, God forbid, his mother. That's all he needed was for Jenny to call his mother. What do you mean he's not home? his mother would shout; his mother always shouted. On Christmas *Eve*, he's not home? Yes, Virginia, for that was his mother's name, your son is not home on Christmas Eve.

That's right, Mom, he thought, I'm here in Los Angeles.

I'd better call Jenny.

He hesitated again, not because he was afraid of Jenny—he did in fact feel invulnerable, invincible, courageous, adventurous, a naked wild man in a luxurious cashmere overcoat—but only because he did not want to spoil his party. He had never had a birthday party in his life because dear Virginia his mother had been inconsiderate enough to become pregnant nine months to the day before Christmas. Who wants to attend anyone's birthday party when the biggest birthday in history is in the midst of celebration? *Next* Year, Virginia would always say, *Next* Year, we'll have some of your friends in later in the day, the afternoon perhaps, or the evening, there's no reason we can't celebrate your birthday just because it happens to fall on Christmas. She had said *Next* Year every year but eventually they ran out of years. By that time he had married Jenny, and not having a birthday party had become habit. Besides, you have to have your birthday parties when you're still a kid wearing glasses. When you're thirty-five and wearing eyeglasses, and then forty and wearing eyeglasses, it doesn't matter a hell of a lot anymore. Until you're about to be forty-two, and still wearing eyeglasses, and a party is about to start and you feel it slipping out of your hands, trickling through your fingers like all the sands of next year, next year, next year—and you want it to be *this* year, *now*.

He was not afraid of Jenny, but he was afraid she would spoil his party.

He picked up the phone receiver.

Instead of calling Jenny, he dialed 7 for the valet and was told the valet had gone home, this is Christmas Eve, sir. He asked if the housekeeper had gone home, too, and was informed that a housekeeper was *always* on duty and she could be reached by dialing 4. He dialed 4 and a woman with a foreign accent answered the phone. He could not place the accent.

"Do you have an iron?" he asked.

"An iron? To press?"

"That's right."

"Yes, I have an iron. Why you don't call the valet? He presses."

"He's gone. It's Christmas Eve."

"Oh. You want to press?"

"Yes. I'd like to press my pants because I'm having a party, you see, and they're all wrinkled from the plane ride. I don't like to have a party in wrinkled pants."

"What room you in? I send."

"One-oh-eight," he said.

"You return?"

"Yes, I return," he said.

"Good. I send."

"Good, you send. Thank you."

He hung up. He called the bell captain then and asked if there was a liquor store in the hotel. The captain told him he could order liquor in the pharmacy, which sounded like a peculiar place

to be ordering liquor, but he hung up and then dialed the operator and asked for the pharmacy. When he was connected, he told
whoever answered the phone that he wanted two bottles of scotch
sent to room 108 and charged to his bill.

He did not begin pressing his suit with the borrowed steam iron
until after the whiskey was delivered. He poured a stiff double
hooker into one of the glasses that were ranged on the counter top
facing the entrance door, and then discovered there was an ice-
making machine under the counter, this was *some* hotel all right.
From the bathroom, he took a clean towel and spread it out on
the counter and then put his trousers on top of the towel and
began pressing them while he sipped at the scotch.

The idea was to keep the party going. He did not know what
his next move would be after he pressed his pants and his jacket,
but he did know that he had two bottles of whiskey and he would
not be forty-two for almost an hour, so the idea was to keep the
party going. Maybe he would just dial the operator and ask her to
ring several rooms in the hotel and when he got them he would
say, "Hi, this is Doc Pitt in room 108. I'm having a little birthday
party, and I wonder if you'd like to come down and join me. It's
right off the pool, room 108." Maybe he'd do that, though he
doubted it. What he *would* do was press his pants and his jacket,
and maybe his tie as well, and then have a few drinks and then
leave this nice hotel room and see what Beverly Hills was all
about.

The telephone rang.

He propped up the steam iron, started for the phone, decided
he'd better be more careful, went back to unplug the iron, and
then ran to the phone to answer it.

"Hello," he said, wondering who would be calling him in Los
Angeles since he didn't know a soul out here but the movie stars.

"Sir," a very nice cultured Choate voice said, "I'm awfully sorry
to be calling you, but would you mind lowering your radio?"

"My *what?*" he said.

"Your radio, sir. I'm terribly sorry, but the guest in the room
next door is trying to nap, and it seems your radio is on very
loud."

"My radio isn't on at *all,*" he said. "*Not* at *all.*"

"Just a moment, sir."

He waited.

"Sir?"

"Yes?"

"Is this Mr. Pitt in room 108?"

"Yes, this is Arthur Pitt in room 108, that's right. *That* part of it is absolutely right."

"Mr. Pitt, would you mind lowering your radio, sir?"

"Listen, are you a cretin?" Arthur asked. "I just told you that my radio is not on. *Not* on. *Off*. I am pressing my pants and drinking some scotch, and my radio is not on. It is off. O-double F. Off."

"Sir, the guest who made the complaint is in the last room on the floor, and your room is the only room next door, so it *must* be your radio, sir."

"Is this a gag?" Arthur asked suspiciously.

"No, sir."

"Then perhaps you would like to take a walk down here and see for yourself, *listen* for yourself, I mean. My radio is off. Do you hear a radio?"

"No, sir, but the guest in 109 . . ."

"Yes, well you tell the guest in 109 that my radio is off."

"Yes, sir, if you say so."

"Thank you. This is *some* hotel," he said, and hung up. Boy, he thought, how do you like that? How the hell do you like that? I'm standing here in my undershorts, minding my own business, and some fat old bastard with a cigar begins having auditory hallucinations and calls the desk to tell me to turn off my radio which isn't even on, boy this is some hotel all right, I'm telling you.

Angrily, he walked back to the counter, plugged in the steam iron, picked up the half-filled glass of scotch, and drained it. Boy, he thought. Next door, he heard the phone ringing. That would be the desk clerk from Choate who would be calling 109 to report that 108 said his radio was not on. The phone stopped ringing. 109 had answered it. Arthur stood silently with the steam iron in one hand and tried to hear the conversation next door. He could not hear a word, some hotel. Well, I'd better press my pants, he thought, and get the hell out of here before they call again to say the wild party in my room has simply got to stop. He ran the iron over his trousers several more times, held them up to examine them, and then pulled them on. They were nice and warm, they made him feel very cozy. He went to the closet for his jacket, studied it when he took it off the hanger, and decided it did not need pressing. He poured himself a very tiny shot of scotch, drank it down, figured he'd have just one more tiny one before leaving the room, and was pouring it over the cubes in his glass when his telephone rang again.

Choate again, he thought. He decided to turn up the radio full blast before answering the telephone, and then did not do it. "Hello," he said into the receiver.

"Mr. Pitt? This is the desk clerk again."

"Well, this is a surprise," Arthur said.

"Mr. Pitt, I wanted to apologize. I spoke to the young lady in 109, sir, and apparently there was some mistake. Apparently what she heard were the loudspeakers around the pool, sir, and she thought it was the radio in the room next door. I'm terribly sorry if I inconvenienced you, sir."

"That's quite all right," Arthur said, "no inconvenience at all. Where'd you go to school?"

"Sir?"

"What prep school?"

"I didn't go to any prep school, sir. I went to a high school in downtown Los Angeles."

"Oh. Did you ever hear of Choate?"

"No, sir."

"Did you ever hear of the Beverly Hills Hotel?"

"Yes, sir."

"That just goes to show," Arthur said, and hung up. He was smiling. He was having a very good time. So the guest next door in 109 was a young lady, huh? Well, good. Maybe he'd just give her a ring on the telephone and they'd have a little laugh together over the misunderstanding. Why not? This was going to be one hell of a birthday party, and he was going to enjoy every goddamn minute of it until it was over. He did not like to think of it as ever being over, especially now when it had just really started, so instead of thinking about it he went back to the counter and poured himself the drink he had promised himself, though not as tiny as he had promised. He drank it down, said, "Ahhhhh," and was putting on his jacket when the telephone rang again.

"Hello," he said into the receiver. "Just a minute, I forgot to unplug the iron."

He went back to the counter, unplugged the iron, poured himself another drink while he was there, and then carried the glass back to the phone with him.

"Yes?" he said.

"This is the bell captain, sir."

"Yes, hello, what can I do for you?"

"I've got a bottle of champagne for you, sir."

"You have?" Arthur said, astonished. "Who's it from?"

"I don't know, sir. It was delivered just a few moments ago."

"Well, that's very nice," Arthur said. "Put it in an ice bucket and send it on over, why don't you?"

"Yes, sir," the bell captain said, and hung up.

Still astonished, Arthur sat on the edge of his bed, certain that the champagne had been ordered by the hotel management who, in their haste to set things right after the recent misunderstanding, were now outdoing themselves lavishly. Well, never look a gift horse, he thought. A party is in progress, and we need all the champagne we can get, not to mention several satin slippers from which to drink it.

The telephone rang again.

He stared at it unbelievingly, thinking the hotel management was really going a bit *too* far, really, and wondering what they had up their sleeves this time. Gardenias? A basket of California oranges? He would flatly refuse. He would say Thank you, your apologies are accepted, but if you send any further gifts, I will have to consider us engaged.

Giggling, he lifted the receiver. "Hello?" he said.

"Is this Mr. Pitt in room 108?"

"Yes, this is he," he said.

"I'm sorry, Mr. Pitt."

"That's quite all right, no need to apologize."

"This is the bell captain again, sir. I'm sorry about that bottle of champagne, sir, but it isn't for you, after all."

"Oh?"

"It's for the young lady in 109, sir. I rang the wrong room, sir, I'm terribly sorry."

"That's all right."

"I'm sorry, sir. Merry Christmas."

"Merry Christmas to you," Arthur said, and hung up.

He felt suddenly demolished. The idea that the champagne was not for him at all but rather for the young lady in 109, the idea that a gift had been extended to him and then just as abruptly withdrawn filled him with a despair that was unbearable. I'd better call Jenny, he thought, what the hell.

He picked up the phone receiver.

He was studying the holes in the dial, trying to decide which one would connect him with the long-distance operator, when he heard the splash outside his window. He thought at once that someone had fallen into the pool; it was still winter in his mind, and people did not voluntarily jump into a swimming pool on Christmas Eve. He immediately replaced the receiver and ran to the sliding glass door, peering through at the pool and the lanai area. At first, he couldn't see anyone either in the pool or around it. Soft recorded violin music was being piped over the loudspeakers. He could see the muted lights illuminating the palms surrounding the pool, and the single immense white Christmas tree in the pocket formed by the U of the hotel's wings—but no one in the pool or around it. And then a head burst through the water and a blonde girl surfaced and swam to the side of the pool, swinging herself up over its tiled lip, and gracefully walking toward the diving board. She was wearing a black, two-piece bathing suit, not a bikini, but cut very low on her waist, the halter top scarcely containing her breasts. She flicked her head to one side, the long mop of blonde hair flapping soddenly away from her face, and then continued walking with that peculiarly graceful flatfooted stamp of athletes and dancers, one hand cupping thumb and forefinger over her nose to clear it, the other tugging the seat of her trunks down over the partially exposed white swell of her buttocks. She mounted the ladder to the diving board and walked to its end where she stood with her hands on her hips and stared down at the water.

She stood that way for the longest time, absorbed, her head

bent, one hip jutting. He had no idea who she was, could not in fact see her face too clearly in the muted light surrounding the pool. But she was tall and blonde and poised, and he could think of only one person in all of Los Angeles who was tall and blonde and very poised. It seemed entirely possible to him that she, who else could it be, had come directly to this fine hotel where after her long and tedious flight she had attempted to take a nap only to be awakened by the poolside music—whereupon she had instantly ordered herself a bottle of champagne, of course, and decided on a midnight swim instead. The girl standing still and serene on the end of the board could not conceivably be anyone but Miss Iris Radley, a strange name for a Swedish girl, and what a pleasant surprise, even though he could not yet see her face, who else could she *possibly* be?

More and more convinced, he watched her captured in reverie, her head and body motionless, her blonde hair glittering with reflected light. At last, she heaved a long sigh, her shoulders moving —he could almost hear that long mysterious sigh through the closed plate glass door—and walked back to the ladder. Her body was tight and slim and tanned, she glided through the soft California night and then turned a short pirouette and moved forward suddenly, not running, drifting, moving magically to the very end of the board. Her knee came up, she made a precise figure four with one taut straight leg, one bent, sprang and hung suspended, the board vibrating beneath her. Head back, body arched, arms wide, she hung against the night for an eternity, and then plummeted to the water below, her arms and hands coming together an instant before she disappeared. He watched. She surfaced some ten feet beyond and then swam in an easy crawl to the shallow end of the pool, executed a clean racer's turn, swam to the deep end, turned again, and continued swimming back and forth tirelessly, effortlessly.

He watched her world.

There was in that world all the things he had never known, the burlesque queen he had not had in Buffalo that time, the birthday gifts that blended with Christmas gifts and left a strange aching void, the bottle of champagne offered and then withdrawn. He wanted to call out to her, wanted to shout, "Hey, are you *really*

Miss Radley who said my hands were cold? Are you really the girl in 109? Hey, how would you like to come to my party? How's the water?"

Trembling, he looked at his watch. It was seven minutes to midnight in White Plains. He would be forty-two years old in seven minutes.

Go ahead, he thought. Call Jenny.

He reached for the stem of his watch and pulled it out. Slowly and carefully, he set the watch back to ten fifty-three, and then nine fifty-three, and then eight fifty-three. He snapped the stem back into the case with a small final click, walked swiftly to the sliding door, and pulled it open.

The girl was just coming out of the water.

He knew goddamn well she was not Miss Iris Radley, and possibly not even the girl in 109. But his step was curiously light, and his heart was beating wildly as he hurried toward the pool to invite her to his party.

YOU'RE ALL WET!

WILLIAM JOHNSTON

It used to be that when you were attacked by a compulsive need to get water in your ears, you could go dunk your head in the bathroom sink. And without suffering any damage to your reputation. Your friends and relatives, in fact, would consider that you had done the right thing.

"Old Fred knew what he had to do and he did it," they would say—not without pride.

But fashions change. Progress stumbles on. Yesterday's conformity is today's eccentricity. Or, to put it another way, how many men do you see on the streets today wearing spats? Not more than a half-dozen at most. And, of these, two are coming home from a costume party.

So it is, too, with wetting the ears. If, today, you feel that you *have* to do it, you can no longer simply pop into the bathroom, dunk and get it over with. Not if you want to keep your seat on the stock exchange. For that kind of behavior is looked upon as a sure sign of acute Wingism (either Right or Left, according to who your enemies are).

No, the only socially acceptable means of getting water in your ears these days is to take up water skiing.

People who constantly dart into and out of bathrooms, dunking their heads, are eventually locked up. The advantage of water skiing, then, is that water skiers, considered Sportsmen, get to ogle a great many girls in bikinis.

Having come this far, let us assume that you are one of those people who needs an occasional wetting of the eardrums and that you have an aversion to being locked up. In other words, let us assume that you have an unquenchable desire to take up water skiing.

If all that is true, then I can help you. Or, to put it another way, I can hinder you. For, after years of experience at the sport, I probably know as much or as little about it as anyone—and when I say "anyone," I do not rule out either the late Dr. Schweitzer or the late Calvin Coolidge, as other so-called experts are apt to do.

If you are really serious about this, the first thing you will need is a touch of whimsy in your soul. Because it is obvious that skiing was never meant to be done on water. Skiing is for snow. Snow stands up; it is relatively solid. Water, on the other hand, offers about as much support as Barry Goldwater at a Democratic convention. You can't step out of the bathhouse, glide across the sand and then, unassisted, go skimming blithely over the waves. If you try it, you will find that you have inadvertently taken up skin diving rather than water skiing.

So, even before you think about purchasing your first pair of skis, it is necessary to convince yourself that you are *not* going to look like a damn fool driving out toward the ocean with a pair of skis strapped to the roof of your automobile.

It won't be easy. But it can be done. I accomplished it by carting my youngest son's sled back and forth between his wading pool and his sandbox. After a week of that, under the questioning eyes of the neighbors, I felt that I could remain serene—at least inwardly—in even the most incongruous situation.

Now that your mind is hardened, the next step is to purchase those skis. Fortunately, the price is reasonable. You can raise the money by skipping lunches during the summer months. Or by robbing the office petty cash fund.

The next thing to do after acquiring your water skis would be to track down the nearest ocean. In the good old days, if you lived in the middle of Death Valley, that would offer somewhat of a challenge. But not so today, since a number of water skiing facilities have been established in some of our driest states. This is done, as I understand it, by digging an enormous ditch, pumping water into it, then setting up a crane-like contraption that pulls the skiers through the water from one end to the other. But if that is water skiing, I am the inventor of Chinese checkers. And, as someone put it to Nicholas Murray Butler when he developed the all-day sucker, "It will never last."

Now then, you are the possessor of your first pair of water skis. And there you will stay. For, unfortunately, it is impossible to operate water skis without the assistance of a motorboat.

The first thing that will occur to you will be that you should get to know someone who actually owns a motordriven runabout of one sort or another. Buying one of your own is out of the question. Most of your petty cash went for skis.

The Motor Boat Association people will make getting acquainted with someone who owns a boat sound ridiculously simple. They will quote you statistics to prove that such people are as thick as fleas (my terminology, not the Association's). The figures may be true. But finding a motorboat owner is not that easy. For they are all clustered in one area—the restricted section of the bathing beach, trying to run down innocent swimmers. If you go looking for them where they are supposed to be—in the boating area—you will get scorched eyeballs before you ever spot one.

The only sensible solution is to rent a boat and inveigle a friend into operating it for you. In time, this will lose you all your friends, but it will also give you the opportunity to learn to water-ski. After all, that's what we're there for, not to coddle the kind of people who sink into a sulk just because someone, in the spirit of constructive criticism, informs them calmly that starboard is "To the right, you blasted ninny! To the right! The right!"

Before approaching either the boat or the ocean, however, it would be well to understand how it is that a pair of skis can support a grown body and remain on top of the water. The theory that this can actually happen is called Captain Andy's Law of Deviated Buoyancy. As Captain Andy himself explained it, "It works like, you know, when a television picture leaves the studio, then flies through the air and skinnies down the antenna and gets into the set. It's the same principle, only it's done with water."

Since you are a beginner, it will be best to start your run from the beach. Those who have had a great deal of experience can start a run from almost anywhere, even from far offshore. But, as a beginner, you will need some firm footing.

Place your skis at the water's edge, with the ends that are curved slightly upward pointing toward the water. Now, slip your bare feet into the footholds until they are secure. Next, lean back, testing your weight against the towrope. Oops, sorry . . . forgot to tell you to bring along a towrope, didn't I?

Well, don't just lie there on your back; pick yourself up and find a towrope. Because the rope, the line that connects you to the boat, is quite necessary. The water skier who neglects to outfit himself with a towrope is the water skier who, having given the go-ahead signal to the boat, finds himself stranded on the beach while the boat disappears into the breakers. It is an awkward feeling; to be avoided, if possible.

Well . . . ready with your towrope? Fine. Grasp it firmly by the handhold. Lean back again, putting your weight against the rope. Now, give the signal to the boatman. You will hear the mighty roar of the engine. The towline will exert a forward thrust. Then, suddenly, almost effortlessly, there you will be—flat on your face in the sand. With the boat disappearing into the breakers.

Before you pick yourself up once more and try again, it might be wise to determine what it was you did wrong the first time. Because, if you don't, you will undoubtedly end up face-down in the sand again. And you don't want that, because, by now, you have a gallery of people watching you.

Your error was that when you felt the forward thrust, you went along with it instead of resisting it. It is the resistance, your skis pushing against the water, that gets you started—and, for all I know, that keeps you going, too. The theory is at least as good as Captain Andy's.

All right, now that you know what you did wrong, let's try again. Remember to resist. And this time, things will go a bit better. This time, you will end up flat on your *back* in the sand. The trouble, clearly, was that you resisted *too much*. I think you're losing your temper.

We don't want you to become discouraged, so we will skip the details of the next few hours. During that time, you will take another half-dozen dives into the sand, dislocate a shinbone, lose your friend who was operating the boat and replace him with a total stranger (who smirks) and turn the amusement of the onlookers into enmity when you begin referring to their collective ancestry in disparaging terms. Let us be kind and assume that those horrible hours have passed and that now you are joyfully— to use a technical phrase—"riding the waves."

The elation will be short-lived. It will last only as long as you remain scared to death. During that period, a very short one, you will pay attention to what you are doing, riding the skis stiffly, keeping your eyes forward, not daring even to twitch. After a few minutes of this, unfortunately, you will gain confidence. You will get fancy.

I blame this on the newsreels. They show water skiers cutting all sorts of didoes, slicing gracefully to the right (starboard), veering artfully to the left (starboard), raising the right (port) ski, raising the left (aft) ski, dodging in and out among the cypress trees and, in general, acting the fool (larboard). The hitch is that these skiers know what they are doing—or, at least, seem to. (It is my honest belief that if they *really* knew what they were doing, if they could see themselves in the newsreels, they would be home in bed reading a good book.)

Be that as it may, you have now gained confidence and are ready to show the gallery that you were really just joshing all along when you were taking those 12-armed, 7-legged dives into the sand. You test your prowess by leaning your body slightly to the left, intending, in this way, to swerve to the left of the boat. Instead, you swerve to the right. No matter. That's how you learn, by making mistakes.

Now, you have the system down pat. Nothing to it. To swerve left, you lean right and vice versa. The next thing is to make a wide sweep, fanning out behind the boat like a spreading peacock tail. You think to yourself that the maneuver will look beautiful from the air—too bad there isn't a planeload of sightseers over-head. Ah, well . . . their loss.

This is the instant when you learn the true portent of those signs along the highway that say "Slippery When Wet." As you lean to either the right or left to go into your wide sweep, you discover that the sea has suddenly turned to glass and that it has been recently waxed.

It is impossible to describe your fall—each water skier falls in his own way. That is the meaning of democracy. The manner isn't important, anyway. What counts is that, confident as you were, you weren't prepared to take another dive. There was not time to count to 10, hold your nose, close your eyes, then reconsider. Sud-denly, you are in the water. But, what is worse, the water is in you. This is when you scold yourself severely for not listening to Mother when she advised you to take that swimming course at the local YM (or W) CA.

After discovering that, where you are, the ocean has no floor, you dogpaddle to the surface, blow your ballast, then look around frantically for your skis. Your skis have been trained by the manu-facturer to free themselves the instant you start to take a header.

The problem here is that, in 80 fathoms of ocean, everything on the surface looks like a ski. This is because your eyes are also at surface level and, so far, it is impossible to climb out of the ocean and mount a ladder to get a better view of the countryside.

So, grasping wildly, you latch onto a slab of driftwood inscribed "Made in Texas by Texans"; an oar from the tug *Mary B. Clausewitz*, out of Merion Station, Pa.; the sixth tentacle (counting from port to starboard) of a feeding octopus; and a bottle with a note in it from one of the airlines suggesting that, at this junction, you would have been happier if you had flown instead of taking a ship.

After an eternity or so, your boat will pull up alongside, nearly swamping you, and the operator will point out the location of your skis. Because you are made of stout stuff (or is it because that strain of insanity in your family is beginning to show itself again?), you will be ready to brave the breakers once more.

In theory, since by now you have lost your confidence completely and with it your lust for derring-do, all should go well from here on out. But that doesn't take into account the nature of the fellow who is at the wheel of your boat. He has become bored and has arbitrarily decided to try a little fancy knitting of his own.

Yonder, Virginia, is an arched bridge. Your captain (they all become captains once they get behind the wheel) is heading directly for the center arch. Or . . . wait a minute . . . perhaps he's steering for the arch to the left of center. Or maybe toward the arch nearest the shore. From where you are, it is impossible to tell exactly what he has in mind—does he *really* think he can leap the bridge?

Eventually, of course, you have to make a decision—which arch to steer for? Statistics show that nine times out of eight you will be wrong. So, it's either another dunking or, if your luck and presence of mind have deserted you, a nice long sojourn at Blair General Hospital, watching Dr. Kildare mug into the camera while he's supposed to be setting your fractured port toe.

Despite the travail, in time, you and your skis will be drawn back to the water. For there is something irresistible about the sport once you have got your feet (and ears) wet. Perhaps it is man's destiny. After all, if the good Lord hadn't meant us to waterski, He would have filled all the oceans with snow.

A BLOW FOR FREEDOM

✒ ERIC KEOWN

It was a dull and brutish day. The library of the club was stuffy, morgue-like and full of retired tea-planters paddling gingerly in their football pools. Since an injudicious lunch my metabolism had proceeded inharmoniously. I felt despondent about the inner meaning of being.

"Mr. Bingle!" keened a page-boy, taking no natural pleasure in this privileged rupture of the silence rule. He looked very sad. It came home to me with poignancy how black the hours must be when most of them are spent trailing up and down stairs bawling for Mr. Bingle who are probably in Aberystwyth. My heart went out to the little lad.

"Mr. Bingle!" he cried again, but without hope.

I beckoned him over to the chair in which I lay prone.

"Someone has need of me?" I asked.

It was good to see his eyes brighten. Perhaps I was his first triumph.

"Wanted on the 'phone, sir."

"By whom?"

"Dunno, sir."

I strode with him firmly down the stairs. My prompting had been nothing but humane. I looked forward to being Mr. Bingle.

"There y'are, sir," said the boy, proudly pointing to a box.

"Find out who it is." Prudence sets some limits, beyond which I felt lay Mrs. Bingle.

"It's a Mr. 'Arris, sir," he whispered.

"Ha, Harris," I said.

"You've been a long time, Bingle," came a voice sharply, a voice to which I failed altogether to take.

"I was polishing my nails in the slumber-room," I said.

131

"You sound very funny. Sort of muffled."

"It's always the same with double pneumonia."

"Double—?"

"Pneumonia. Spent the night on the Embankment. Been out with the boys."

"Look here, Bingle, I don't like your tone."

"That's what they all said in Harley Street this morning."

The man at the other end, whom I judged to have a lumpish diamond in his tie, could be heard making a great effort at restraint.

"How are things going?" he rasped.

"Very slowly," I told him.

"You know how anxious we are to get this affair settled?"

"So am I," I said warmly. "I'm sick and tired of it."

"Buckwheat considers it extremely urgent."

"Buckwheat is a damned fool," I said.

"Really, Bingle!"

Did I nevertheless detect a note of respect, even of anxiety, which had been quite lacking from his original remarks? I rather thought I did. It seemed to me Bingle had been playing his cards badly. He appeared to be in some kind of key-position, and yet to be permitting this Harris to walk all over his face. A practical sympathy with Bingle and his dependents seized me.

"I honestly don't know if I can be bothered to go on," I said.

"Bingle, your attitude amazes me!"

"It doesn't me," I said, "I've been going into the profits."

"We've been over all that before."

"Let's go all over it again. If you put my slice on a butter-dish it wouldn't show."

"Buckwheat and I feel we are being more than generous, Bingle."

"But even if it were ten times as big, after the offer I've had today from America I don't see how I can afford not to ask you and Buckwheat to take a running jump at yourselves."

There was an ugly hydraulic sound at the other end, wherever that might be.

"America? Not Gumstein?"

"That's neither here nor there," I said. Nor was it. I refreshed myself with a little snuff, of a blend first concocted for the pleasure of Queen Victoria's mother, and waited.

"Bingle, old boy, I wonder if you're free for dinner?"

"I'm dining with a gorilla at the House of Lords."

"Because we mustn't be hasty about all this, must we? You know how much Buckwheat and I value your services."

"You bet I do," I said.

"Suppose we double your whack?"

"I could go back and finish polishing my nails."

"Come, old boy, a joke's a joke."

"I have known that for a long time."

"Look here, I don't know what old Buckwheat'll say, but will you carry on if we treble?"

"I might," I said. "If I have it in writing by to-morrow morning."

"I say, you are a tiger, Bingle!"

"Aren't I?" I said, and hung up.

And now I suppose I must look for another club.

ONE HALF OF TWO
ON THE AISLE

ᴈ§ JEAN KERR

In my short and merry life in the theatre, I have discovered that there are two sharply contrasting opinions about the place of the drama critic. While in some quarters it is felt that the critic is just a necessary evil, most serious-minded, decent, talented theatre people agreed that the critic is an unnecessary evil. However, if there is some room for argument about the value of the critic, there is none whatever about the value of the critic's wife. To the producer, in particular, it is painful enough that the reviewer must bring his own glum presence to the theatre, but the thought that he will also bring his wife and that she, too, will occupy a free seat is enough to cool the cockles of his heart and send him back on a soft diet. "What if a doctor had to bring his wife along when he performed an operation?" he will ask you. "Can't you see her sitting there murmuring, 'Here's a nice suture, dear, and why don't you try this clamp?'"

In their innermost souls, the producer and the press agent are convinced that the wife has a bad effect on the critic and consequently a bad effect on the notice. Of course, not all critics have wives; some of them habitually attend the theatre in the company of pretty actresses, a practice which is thought to be not only suitable but even, on occasion, inspiring.

It isn't that anyone believes a wife's influence is direct or intentional. Presumably no one has suggested that it is her practice to tuck her spouse into a cab at eleven o'clock with the stern admonition, "Now you hurry right back to that little office and say what a bad play this was, hear?" No, the whole thing is much more intangible than that, and I'm afraid it boils down to the sobering fact that the producer feels that the mere physical presence of a wife depresses the critic, lowers his spirits, clogs his areas of good will, and leaves his head rattling with phrases like "witless," "tasteless," and "below the level of the professional theatre."

On the other hand, just let some wife absent herself from the happy revelers at an opening and you will see consternation settle like a fine dew upon producer and press agent alike. Souls are searched. Old wounds are probed. Is the jig up? Have runners been coming in from Philadelphia with the bad word? Have those preview audiences been squealing? Clearly somebody talked. The lady has had fair warning and is at home with a good book.

It is my impression that my own attendance record is rather higher than the average. This can be explained by the fact that I have those four small children and naturally have to get out a lot. When my husband first went on a newspaper, and for several years thereafter, I brought my lark-like disposition and gooey good will to every single solitary show that opened. Lately, however, I've begun to develop a small, cowardly instinct for self-preservation, and I find that there are two kinds of plays I can bear not to see: plays about troubled adolescents who can't find themselves, and plays about the Merchant of Venice.

During this past summer we paid a visit to Stratford, England, and saw a number of plays not including *The Merchant of Venice.* It seemed to make the whole trip worth while. I have friends, old-time theatregoers who have seen every Hamlet since Forbes-Robertson, and they love to sit around and reminisce about the way Leslie Howard played the ghost scene and how Gielgud read the speech to the players. Now, I hope to spend my twilight years reminiscing about the Shylocks I haven't seen. Donald Wolffit, Luther Adler, Clarence Derwent—oh, it's a splendid gallery already and I expect to add to it before I'm through.

As everyone knows, one of the chief problems of going to the theatre with a critic is getting out of there a split second after the curtain comes down or, if the show is a very long one, a split second before. Lately I've become very adept at judging the precise line of dialogue on which to start pulling the sleeves of my coat out from under the lady next to me. This might be when an actress says, "In future years, when you speak of me, be kind," or when an actor says, "Now that I've got you, darling, I'll never let you go," although I have known shows in which he let her go for another ten minutes after that.

Then follows a wild scramble down a dark and crowded aisle. I used to forge stolidly ahead, having developed a technique for this sort of thing in Ohrbach's basement, but one night, when I felt I had Walter firmly by the hand and was propelling him out into the traffic, I heard a plaintive voice muttering, "Hey, lady, gee, lady, please!" I looked up to discover that I had Farley Granger firmly by the hand. It's things like that that make one pause and reconsider.

After the show, most wives go out with their friends or go home to their peaceful apartments. I tag along to the office because we live in Larchmont and neither one of us wants to make the trip back alone. Obviously, if I were planning to influence my husband, my golden opportunity would come during the cab ride over to the office. The only trouble is that he immediately assumes the yogi-like silence and the glazed manner of a sandhog in a decompression chamber.

I used to think he was going into shock, but I have gradually gleaned that he is just trying to think of an opening sentence. I wouldn't dream of breaking the cathedral hush that surrounds us. However, if there is one thing a cab driver does not seem to recognize, it is a cathedral hush. All the cab drivers we get at ten forty-five in the evening are sports, bon vivants, and raconteurs. One man the other night had a really tantalizing story about how he had to drive a burro to Riverdale. My only question is, where are all those gay blades during the six-o'clock rush hour in front of the Biltmore?

Once my husband is at his desk, he sets to work immediately, furiously consulting the dozens of penciled notes he makes during the show on intricately folded yellow paper. I glanced at the notes one evening and the first one said, "Why he shedelepp so often, especially in the speckeldiff?" I only hope he doesn't lose them some night. They might be found, and how would he prove they're not atomic secrets?

Anyway, while he's working, I'm not idle. I sit at an empty desk and read back copies of *The Hollywood Reporter* and draw horses. Sometimes I chat with bright young copyboys, who, it would appear, are serious students of the theatre. The only difficulty is that they want to discuss Toller and Strindberg, whereas, at that hour of the morning, I want to discuss Lindsay and Crouse. Occasionally someone wants to know why Kafka's *The Trial* is never done. Of course I have no figures here, but I have this feeling that it is done all the time. Maybe not.

Then, too, my husband sometimes consults me while he's writing a review. A hoarse shout will come over the partition, "Hey, how do you spell desiccate?" But this is patently ridiculous. If I could spell desiccate I would long since have assumed my rightful place in the world of letters.

An interesting aspect of dramatic criticism is that an actor can remember his briefest notice well into senescence and long after he has forgotten his phone number and where he lives. Thus it is quite a common occurrence for a critic to meet a nice young thing at a party and have her say, "Oh, don't you remember me? You saw me in *The Squared Circle* four years ago and you said I was 'earnest, effortful, and inane.'" Well, that's what makes cocktail parties so interesting.

On the other hand, most people who read more than one drama critic quickly forget who said what. We had an interesting demonstration of this last summer when we met a film actress who was chatting wisely and wittily about the theatre until she reached the subject of a certain musical comedy. Then she declared with some heat, "I don't know what gets into Brooks Atkinson sometimes. Do you know what he said about that show?"

Whereupon she proceeded to recite from memory two paragraphs, word for word, semicolon for semicolon, of Walter's review. After the brief hush that followed this recital, I murmured, "Did Brooks really say that? Well, there you are—even Homer nods," the while my husband made little clicking sounds indicating that he was too shocked even to comment.

In common with the wives of other critics, I am so anxious to indicate that I in no way influence or attempt to influence my husband's opinions that I rather overstate the case and perhaps give the impression that we never discuss the theatre at all—that our conversation is exclusively concerned with stories about our adorable children and the cute way they spilled Three-in-One oil all over the living-room rug, interspersed occasionally with highlights from the world of sport.

The fact is that we have many an intelligent discussion of the play coming home on the train, at which time I have a carbon copy of the review to read. A typical opening gambit in such a conversation would be: "Boy! If *that* was a haunting, luminous performance . . . !"

PINK TIES

❧ ALEXANDER KING

There was one curious aspect to my life during the years from 1917 to 1948 which I have somehow or other forgotten to mention to you before—that for more than thirty years I wore only pink neckties. Not ever any other color, under any circumstances. It finally got to be an identifying trademark for me, although, heaven is my witness, I never intended anything of the sort when I first started wearing them. In fact, I got into this pink-tie addiction when I was only seventeen years old, and believe me, any boy or man who was willing to wear such an unorthodox color back in those dark days of somber men's attire had to have plenty of guts or plenty of stupidity, or plenty of both, to get away with it.

Of course I stumbled into it all, as I fell into most things, by strictly minding my own business, and by just carefully putting one foot in front of the other.

I was working on the New York *Sunday World* when I was seventeen, and I was also doing some cartooning jobs for the *Big Stick*, a Jewish joke paper that I already told you about. My salary on the *World* was twenty-five dollars a week, and I generally took long, leisurely walks every Friday afternoon, just to give myself, and those twenty-five bucks, a luxurious airing. These walks often included window-shopping tours ranging from Nassau Street and lower Broadway to Forty-second Street and Fifth Avenue up as far as the Plaza.

Well, then, loaded as I was, one of those Friday afternoons I happened to stop in front of Sulka's window, somewhere in the Forties or Fifties, and I noticed that they were having a sale of neckties. Six dollars a tie. I wondered what in hell they could possibly have charged for them before the sale. I felt myself getting even a little indignant about the whole thing. However, in spite of my simmering annoyance I found that I was deliberately walking into their cool, expensive-smelling store.

It stands to reason, doesn't it, that I wasn't planning to buy anything, and the clerk, whose face looked just like a shinbone with eyebrows, knew this as well as I did. But, like two idle dogs of the same gender who can't resist their pointless browsing, this clerk and I forthwith proceeded to give the stock a judicious fingering; which means that I sneered disparagingly at the tie-racks while he kept on constructing smart four-in-hand knots in mid-air, just to show off his really stupendous manual dexterity, and also to make me feel like a cheap piker.

This went on for about twenty minutes or so, and I was just about to call off the whole silly ballet by making my exit, when the clerk, who was obviously a pansy, suddenly said to me, "You know, we have some colors that are much less popular, and those ties cost only one dollar apiece. Would you care to see any of them?"

"Why not?" I said. "As long as I'm here, anyway. What sort of colors are they?"

"I'll show them to you. To tell you the truth," he said with a confidential smirk, "I'm saving some of them especially for my friends."

This, of course, instantly alarmed me, because I was quite sure that any friend of his was bound to be a leaping faggot, but just the same I decided to take a look. He pulled a box off the shelf, removed the lid, and exposed about two dozen crepe-de-Chine ties, all of them pink.

"Not a very great selection," I said. "How much are they, did you say?"

"A dollar apiece," he said. "They cost us more than that wholesale."

Now, then, who really knows what dark and sinister impulses are crouched and coiled in the recesses of man's unconscious? Who can guess what terrible unfulfilled longings in a man's heart are just waiting for the right word, or the right moment, to spring into instant, demoniacal action, for the sake of a long-deferred secret appeasement?

In short, I bought six of those pink crepe-de-Chine neckties, and, believe it or not, I even had a certain feeling of high accomplishment out of this demented proceeding. It was as if I'd pulled a particularly cute caper, not just on Sulka and Company, but on all the goddamned expensive shops up and down Fifth Avenue.

And that's how it happened that I came to wear a pink tie to work the next day. I labored, at the time, in the tower of the old Pulitzer Building, down on Park Row, and, when I first took off my coat, the screams, the whistles, the yowls and the yodelings all around me stopped all human activity on that floor for the next ten minutes.

But, since I was seventeen years old and a man of my convictions, I ignored this racket and quietly went about my business. My business was to make some black-and-white line sketches for the Sunday magazine section, and so I was able, for a while at least, to bend zealously over my drawing board, without having to meet anybody's eye. This was certainly a help, but even so it was hard for me to ignore the mad cavortings of the office boys and the various younger staff members, who made it their pleasure to pass my desk forty times an hour in that special mincing gait which has ever been the immemorial hallmark of the camping fairy.

I don't know how I lived through that first morning. At any rate, right before lunch I took off my tie and hung it in a metal closet where I usually kept only a pair of torn rubbers. When I got ready to quit work that evening, I had a shocking surprise waiting for me. Somebody on that floor had dipped my tie in a large glue vat that was permanently stationed near the fire exit. The glue had completely dried up and left the tie with a texture like a smoked kipper; but since I knew that a lot of furtive eyes were certainly watching me at that moment, I just dropped my violated neckpiece casually into the garbage can and went home.

Fools! I thought. Just a pack of crude, conventional fools. Ah, well, they believed I was routed, did they? They thought they had me down for the count, eh? Well, they'd soon learn different. Damned soon, too! I'd show those mushheads a thing or two—or even five, if it came to that, because, as you perfectly well know, I still have five more of those ties hanging at home in my closet, ready and waiting to be launched whenever the spirit moved me.

I was determined to teach all those dopes a lesson, to teach them to respect a man's right to wear whatever the hell he goddamned well pleased. And so the battle lines were drawn, and no mercy was given or expected.

I wore my pink ties every day from then on, and, do you know, as the tense weeks went by a very funny thing happened. In about a month or so, I couldn't help but notice that slowly, ever so slowly, the fury and the clamor were beginning to die down. In fact, by the time I'd gotten around to wearing the third of my ties, somebody from the business office, who had never before seen my colorful haberdashery and was just about to launch himself into the gibbering state of epilepsy that the occasion seemed to call for, was stupefied into silence when a few of my nearby colleagues told him to shut his trap and to mind his own goddamned business.

You see, the young journalists on my floor had not only become used to my pink ties, they had developed a certain comradely state of tolerance toward my special eccentricity. They had come to consider it *their* peculiar privilege to razz me for acting out of line, but they all stood defensively by me if any unlicensed outsider ever decided to put me down.

In short, after six months of nothing but pink ties, nobody around me seemed any longer to notice that I was wearing anything out of the ordinary at all.

And then came a real crisis. I gave five of my ties away to be cleaned, in a store on West Eighth Street, and when I came back a few days later to reclaim them, I found to my horror that the place had been completely gutted by fire.

It was a real calamity for me, as you can plainly understand. Those pink ties were the symbols of my individuality, weren't they? And, to a certain extent, they had even become the tangible pennants that I had tremblingly fluttered before a hostile world, to announce my freedom of choice. I just couldn't let myself down now. I simply couldn't make my appearance at the office wearing some dark, practical colors, not after all I'd already been through, could I? If I did, all would be lost again.

Oh, yes, I could just see all those blubberheads on the paper saying, "Well, you've finally got yourself straightened out! Decided to rejoin the human race again, eh? Good for you, boy!"

No, no, no! It was out of the question. Eternal vigilance was the price of freedom! That was the basic rule of the game, and I damn well knew it.

And so, in this frightening emergency, I quickly hustled up to B. Altman's on Thirty-fourth Street, and bought myself three yards of candy-pink crepe-de-Chine material. Afterward I consulted a classified phone directory and found that the Acme Tie Company, right nearby, on Thirty-sixth Street, was prepared to make neckties in small quantities to private order.

I had myself quite a time finding that goddamned tie place, too, because it was located in one of those depressing blocks between Eighth and Ninth avenues, where there weren't even any drugstores or lunchrooms to break up the solid façade of grim wholesale manufacturing. I did find it at last, and it was, literally, just a very small hole in a very thick and forbidding wall.

Mr. Aron Buxbaum, the owner, turned out to be a neat little bearded elderly Jew who wore a black skullcap and satin sleeve garters, and who showed no surprise whatever at the unusual color of my material.

"I'm in a terrible hurry about these ties," I told him as I unwrapped the stuff. "How soon can I possibly have them?"

"Day after tomorrow," said Mr. Buxbaum. "We generally like to have more time, but, if it's an emergency, we'll just do the best we can."

"Fine," I said. "I'll pick them up around lunchtime on Friday."

When I returned, two days later, Mr. Buxbaum handed me a pretty good sized package, and a bill for fifteen dollars.

I nearly fainted. "How come, fifteen dollars?" I said. "You're charging me a fortune. After all, I supplied the material, didn't I?"

Mr. Buxbaum looked hurt. "We do very fine work here," he said. "You just take a look at those ties, and you'll see what you're getting for your money. You're getting a big bargain."

"Never mind," I said. "I haven't got time now, I have to get back to work. I don't get through until four o'clock."

Luckily, because it was payday, I had a twenty-dollar bill on me, and so I was able to square myself.

"Wear them in good health!" said Mr. Buxbaum, when I finally stood in the open doorway.

"Thanks," I said. "By the way, how many ties did you manage to get out of that material, anyway?"

"Exactly sixty-two," he said. "If you had bought just a quarter of a yard more, you could have had sixty-five."

And that's how it was.

Ties, I later learned, are cut on the bias and really require very little material. And so, at one stroke, I had added to my wardrobe a matter of more than five dozen pink ties.

They lasted for quite a while, too, and when they finally wore out I just bought some more material and had a new batch made up for myself over at Buxbaum's. And that's how it happened that I came to march through the ages as a peculiarly necktied man.

And then, sometime in 1947, all of my luggage was lost by one of the airlines, and I arrived in New York with only one pink necktie to my name, the one that I was wearing. Well, I naturally went straight up to Altman's to get myself three and a quarter yards of fresh pink crepe-de-Chine. I'd made these trips and these purchases quite often during the past thirty years, and I no longer had the slightest difficulty in locating the Acme Tie Company on West Thirty-sixth Street.

But when I finally got there, old man Buxbaum wasn't anywhere in sight. Instead, a sort of young and beardless caricature of him was sitting against the back wall and making entries in a huge ledger.

"You're Mr. Buxbaum's son, aren't you?" I said.

"Yes," he said. "I'm George Buxbaum. And you, I believe, must be Mr. King."

"I am," I said. "But how in the world did you know that?"

"Because," said George Buxbaum, "my father is now dead, and you used to be his only customer."

"What?" I said. "You mean that I alone have kept his whole enterprise going?"

"If you want to put it that way," he said. "Actually, the matter is a little more complicated than that. You see, my brothers and I are probably the largest wholesale tie manufacturers in America. In fact, we own this building, which houses one of our four factories."

"And what about this store?" I said.

"Ah, well, that was all my father's wish," he said. "You see, he came to this country as an immigrant and started to sell ties out of a cigar box, on Orchard Street. My mother used to make those ties on a foot-pedal sewing machine at home. Later on he got a pushcart, and by the time my brothers and I were going to high school he'd managed to get himself a nice little store on Second Avenue near Twelfth Street. Well, to make a long story short, we all of us somehow or other got into the necktie business, and we did so well in it that after a while the whole family kept pleading with my father to retire, to take it easy, or at least to take some kind of an executive position in one of our plants. But, for some reason or another, he just never had any real confidence in our success. It was all too big and much too vague for him. Everything was done by bank drafts and checks, and in our places of business he never saw any real money changing hands; and so, every time we expanded, or opened a new factory, he just got more worried about us.

"Finally, one day he pleaded with us to fix him up this little retail place right here, where he at least could go on making a real visible dollar across the counter. I think he felt that he was prepared to save the family from absolute ruin, when we had all smashed up with our grand and highfalutin notions. So we built this store for him, and for a while he even had a couple of dozen customers that used to trade here steadily. But for the last eight or ten years, the only jobs that came his way were your pink ties.

"And that brings me to still another point," he said. "You see, Mr. King, the whole family always gets together for dinner in my mother's house on Friday nights, and my father and my brothers and I, we would spend hours and hours, wondering and speculating what could possibly be the meaning of all those pink ties. Some of us thought it must be the emblem of some secret society. Others had the idea that maybe it had a certain religious significance, or something. But my father—you must excuse me for telling you this—my father was convinced that you were an artist, and that you painted naked girls on those ties, and that you sold them at stag parties."

"Your father overestimated my talents," I said. "No. I had those ties made for other good and sufficient reasons." And then I told young Buxbaum, briefly, the gist of my story.

"Well," he said, "I'm very glad you've explained it at last, because if my father's spirit is anywhere at all, it certainly must be hovering around this little store where he spent so many years of his life."

He opened a small desk file, and I could see that it contained only one single card. George Buxbaum showed me what his father had written on it. It was in Yiddish.

KING, ALEXANDER
PINK TIES
ONLY PINK TIES.
WHY?

The children think he is some kind of a bolshevik, but I'm sure he only makes a few harmless dirty pictures. He is a good and steady customer. May God preserve him from mischief. And from the police.

On the bottom of this card young Buxbaum now wrote *Account Closed.*

"So you are finally giving up the store," I said.

"Yes," he said. "By the end of next week the door and window will be walled up, and the premises will have been absorbed by the rest of the building. But don't worry, for old time's sake we'll make you this last batch of ties from the material you just brought. You'll just have to call for them on the seventh floor."

And that was the end of the Acme Tie Company, and that was the last of my pink ties, too, because I never had the heart to take my business to anybody else.

CHOCOLATE FOR THE WOODWORK

◂§ ARTHUR KOBER

The doorbell rang, but no one in the Gross household made the slightest move to answer it. It rang again, clearly and demandingly.

"Nu?" yelled Mrs. Gross from the kitchen, where she was washing the breakfast dishes. "So just because is here Sunday, is a vacation fa evveybody, ha? Listen the way it rings the bell—like a regelleh fecktree fomm lomm clocks. So open op the door, somebody!"

From the bathroom, Bella shouted, "What'sa matter with evveybody arounn here? Are they deef or something? Fa heaven's sakes, can'tcha hear the bell?"

The task of opening the door clearly devolved upon Pa Gross. He angrily threw his newspaper to the floor and got up from his rocker. "Evvey time a persin sits donn to ridd a couple woids in the paper is alluva sumn a big busy here in house. So who is here the soiving goil? Me! . . . Aw right awready!" The last remark was addressed to the clamoring bell. "You can't see I'm coming?"

The man Mr. Gross ushered into the dining room was a study in sartorial splendor. His Panama hat, which he didn't bother to remove, had a band resplendent in many colors. The Palm Beach suit he wore contrasted vividly with his blue shirt, which, together with a blue tie and a carefully folded blue kerchief which peeped from his breast pocket, gave an ensemble effect. Black-and-white sports shoes and purple socks with red vertical stripes completed a dazzling costume. For a moment, Pa stared in wide-eyed wonder at the magnificent stranger, then he sniffed. There was a pervasive odor about the visitor which he quickly identified as turpentine. This, then, must be the long-awaited painter whose magic was

146

going to transform the dingy Gross apartment into a thing of beauty.

"Good munning, good munning!" Pa twinkled at the fashion plate who stood before him. "So you is the paintner the lendludd is sending, no?"

"No! The paintner is woiking fa me." There was implied rebuke in the man's tone. "I'm the *boss* paintner. Wait, I'll give you mine cott." He reached into his inside pocket, whipped out a stained wallet, and from one of its many folds extracted several cards. By this time Mrs. Gross and Bella were standing beside Pa, and the visitor solemnly presented each of them with a card.

The three Grosses studied the slips of pasteboard in their hands. A good portion of them was taken up by a design of an open can with the name "Eagle" on it. Above this was the phrase "Old Dutch Process" and below it the legend "Employ a Good Painter. Good Painters Use White Lead. White Lead Lasts." There was barely enough room left for the name, Philip Rudnick, and an address and telephone number.

While the Grosses examined his card, Mr. Rudnick's attention was devoted to their apartment. With his fingers he dug at a flaky wall, peeling huge hunks from it and leaving a white, gaping wound in a vast field of yellow. "Tchk, tchk, tchk!" Philip Rudnick's oscillating head tacitly rebuked Mr. and Mrs. Gross. "How people can live in such a place! Lookit how is falling donn the wall in liddle pieces." He continued scraping with his fingers. "Some place you got it here! Comes the Boarder Felt and right away you is gung to get a summints!"

"I begya podden!" Bella's voice was hard and chilly. "We happen not to be inarrested in what the Board of Health is gonna do to us. What we happen to be inarrested in is having this here apartment fixed up so that evvey individual or person who comes along won't stick in their two cents' worth of what's wrong with this place. What we wanna know is just what you intend to do regarding the fixing up of this here apartment."

Mr. Rudnick stared at Bella as if seeing her for the first time. Then, turning to Mr. Gross, he said, "The dutter?" Pa nodded. Mr. Rudnick scraped his purple chin with his nails and eyed Bella reflectively. "She is esking what is Rudnick gung to do with this apottment. Listen, lady." He clasped his hands behind his back and rocked on his heels. "You know hommany yirrs is Rudnick in the paintning business? Plenty! You know hommany apottments is Rudnick fixing op? Plenty, believe me!" His voice suddenly became conversational. "I want you should answer me a question. You a woiking goil?"

"Uf cuss!" sang out Pa Gross.

"So what is your line?" Mr. Rudnick asked.

"I happen to be the privitt seckatary fa a very important pardy who is inclined along financial matters," said Bella.

"Aha, a seckatary! So how you would like if your boss say to you, 'How you gung to write the letter you putting donn by you in the shuthend book? You gung to put the paper in the machine with the left hend udder the right hend? You gung to use by you the liddle pinkie udder the whole hend?' 'What's the diffrince?' you is gung to give the boss an enswer. 'Mine job is to write it fa you the lettis. If you like mine job, so is O.K. If you don't like it, then you give me the seck. But how I'm doing the job, that's strickly mine business.'" He waved a finger at Bella. "So the same is with Rudnick. How I'm gung to fix by you the apottment, that's strickly mine business."

"He's positiffly got it right!" declared Pa Gross, placing a hand on the visitor's shoulder. "Mr. Rudnick is foist gung to do the paintning job, then we'll complain when he is finndished."

Mrs. Gross felt it her duty to come to her daughter's defense. "Say, what is here—Europe, maybe, a persin dassent tukk a couple woids? She says something, Bella, and right away is evvey-body yelling on her 'Sharrop!'" She glowered at the two men. "Cossacks!"

Mr. Rudnick, busy blotting the back of his neck with his hand-kerchief, ignored this attack. "Oooh," he complained, "is very hot here in house. Look," he said, "why you so stingy with the winda opening when is here like a regelleh stove?" He walked to the window and raised it. He looked down at the street and then, wildly waving his fist, he cried out, "Hey, you little bestidds, kipp away from mine machine, you hear? In two seconds I'll come downstairs and I'll fix you good, you tramps, you!" He turned away from the window and scowled at the Grosses. "A fine neighborhood you got it here! Some foist-cless gengsters is gung to be the kits in the stritt. I'm leaving mine uttemobill donnstairs—mine machine is a Chevvy," he added parenthetically—"and right away they scretching op by me the machine, the no-good bummers! Where I am living, on the Concuss, is O.K. to leave mine machine a whole day on the stritt and will come no kits to scretch by me the car. But here in this neighborhood—" A shrug of his shoulders completed his comment.

"A lotta people I know," said Bella icily, "they ride with the subway, where they got no worries who scratches up the cars."

"Excuse me!" Mr. Rudnick's tone was laden with disdain. "Evveything I say is with her no good. Now is a sin to have a machine, ha? Today is a paint job in this neighborhood, temorreh is a paint job in that neighborhood, next day is a paint job maybe in the Heights. So the boss paintner shouldn't have a machine? Listen, you think I get maybe pleasure from mine Chevvy? Nah! Is expenses fa ges, is expenses fa tires, is all the time expenses. You know hommuch it custs me, mine expenses? Plenty! And that's with you a sin, ha?"

"Parm me," said Bella, somewhat chastened, "but I happen not to be criticizing whether you have a car or you don't have one. I happen to be criticizing that just because some little kids are playing arounn on the street and your car happens to be in the way, that is no excuse you should indulge in vulgarity or to criticize this neighborhood, which we happen to be living in at the present time."

Mr. Rudnick seemed about to say something sharp and cutting, but thought better of it. "Listen," he said, forcing a smile, "in mine house if mine dutter tukked so fresh to a guest, you know what I would give her? Plenty! But what can a persin speck from this neighborhood?" Before Bella could find a fitting rejoinder he had whipped out a notebook and pencil. "Nu, Rudnick is not here to make spitches. Rudnick is here to see with the paint job." He abandoned the Grosses to inspect the walls. "Paint with stipple finish the whole thing complete," he mumbled as he made notes. "Wash op the cilling, take away the crecks, fix it the loose plester, and don't fegget you should do kelsomine job. With the flurr—scrape, uf cuss, and you should finndish with two coats fomm shel-leck." He headed toward the window and noticed the radiator in passing. "Aha, the radiatiss you should silver op. And with the windiss, take loose puddy away, new puddy put in." Mr. Rudnick continued making notes as he walked from room to room. The Gross family trailed after him, and when he ran his fingers along the woodwork all of them followed suit and nodded discerningly.

The procession returned to the dining room. "O.K.," said Mr. Rudnick, snapping his notebook shut. "Mine paintners will come temorreh to fix it by you the apottment. Will be the place brannew. Will be a pleasure to live here." Again his glance encompassed the room, and he seemed to shudder. "Not like is now."

"What about the matter from the color?" asked Bella. "We haven't decided yet what should be the color of the apartment."

"A question!" jeered the painter. "What should be the color? Chotruse, uf cuss! Ye know what is chotruse?"

"Green," Bella said.

Mr. Rudnick pretended he hadn't heard her. "Chotruse is grinn." This was addressed confidentially to Pa. "Go to the best homes. Go to the finest flets on the Concuss, and is oney one color —chotruse! Mine apottment, where I'm living, is strickly chotruse."

"Well, it so happens I got diffrint idears on the subjeck," said Bella. "It so happens that what we want in the line of color is cream walls—"

"Crimm walls!" bellowed Mr. Rudnick. "Is no more stylish crimm walls! You know where you find crimm walls? In the chipp apottments where is living very common pipple. Feh! But go to the Concuss, go even to the Heights, and you know hommany places is chotruse? Plenty!"

"See here," said Bella, "it's our house. Do you mind leaving us fix it the way we like, inasmuch as we are the folks living here and it so happens you are not?"

Mr. Rudnick eyed her steadily for several seconds. He then turned to Mr. Gross and, nodding in Bella's direction, said, "The boss, ha?"

The old man felt obliged to define his daughter's authority. "She's a single goil. When we fix the apottment like she says, maybe will come here some nice boyess—"

"Fa heaven's sakes, Pa!" Bella screamed. "What's his business that I'm single? Must you tell the whole world who comes here about your own daughter's condition?"

"Dope!" Mrs. Gross's shrill voice was also raised in protest. "Why you don't tell him hommuch money we not yet paying the butcher? Why you don't tell him fomm your gold watch in punnshop? Go on, tell your friend evveything fomm the femily, Mr. Tettletale!"

"Sha, sha, sha!" Mr. Rudnick's features now broke into a disarming smile. "O.K., so now I know how is. So will Rudnick make fa you crimm walls just like the dutter wants it. Now is evveybody serrisfied, and I'm seeing you in the munning."

He started for the hallway, but Bella's next queston arrested him. "What about the woodwork?" she asked. "I want it should be a chawklit color."

"Ha?" Mr. Rudnick's baffled expression indicated he wasn't sure he had heard her correctly.

"I want the color should have two tones," explained Bella. "I want cream fa the walls and chawklit fa the woodwork."

Mr. Rudnick lifted his Panama hat and daintily scraped his scalp with his little finger. "Chucklit!" he murmured. Replacing his hat, he slowly and deliberately took out his notebook, scribbled something in it and then looked up. "Excuse me," he said. "What kine chucklit you would like fa the woodwork—Nestle's udder Hoishey's?"

"See here," said Bella, "I take that remark fomm whence it comes."

"Chucklit!" Mr. Rudnick replaced his book, tapped the crown of his gay Panama with his hand, and stalked to the door. As he was about to leave the apartment, he stopped, stared reflectively into space, and then turned around. "Listen, lady," he shouted at Bella, "Rudnick is gung to fix the place just like you say—two tunns, crimm and chucklit! And listen. If you not finding a nice boy after Rudnick is fixing the apottment, you know what you should put in the chucklit woodwoik? Ammints! You hear me—ammints!"

Bella Gross reached into her arsenal of invective for a particularly annihilating reply, but she was too late. Mr. Rudnick was out of the apartment, leaving behind the ringing echo of his voice shouting "Ammints!"

THE GIRL WITH THE
BEAR RUG EYES

ᴥঌ REX LARDNER

"Call for you on two, Mr. Forrest. Mr. Hank Bullett. You have a luncheon engagement with him at one at the Golden Spoon, sir."

"Thanks, Marilyn . . . Would you please ask one of the girls to pick up the report in my box and pass it on to Mr. Wainwright? . . . Put Mr. Bullett on, please."

"Yessir."

"Hello, Hank?"

"Hi, Phil. That operator of yours got a mighty cuddly voice, you know?"

"I never noticed . . . Listen, Hank, don't we have a lunch date? I want to drop something off with you."

"Yeah, we had one. But listen, old buddy. I got to beg off. I'm hung up."

"Well, OK. I know how busy you educational-TV writers are. How's the show coming?"

"Pretty messy. We're doing mostly schlong stuff now and very little cerebral."

"What the hell is schlong?"

"The messy stuff that you have to wear a raincoat. Pies, flour, soapy water, dripping chocolate. Ratings go up in proportion to how damaged the contestants get. With this new stunt I thought up, we ought to field a twenty-seven. It's a series of races between two husband-wife teams. There's these different-type beds, you know? Cot, sofa, hammock, Louis the Fourteenth with a canopy yet. Which wife can blow up the balloon first and bust it and then the husbands sprint and dive into the beds. Starts out quiet, but they get progressively gooier. Taffy, mud, glue. Screams."

"Who's in shape to do all the diving, for God's sake? A gymnast couldn't do it."

"You'd be surprised at the country's athletes when there's coupons for iceboxes and trips to Hawaii on the line. And schlong gets 'em in the tent, Phil. We're selling plenty skin lotion."

"Where are you now, Hank?"

"In the sack, composing witty lines for B girls. How's this? 'I like older men bec—' "

"What the hell are you doing in the sack at noon? Why aren't you at the office, stirring hot pitch for the husbands of America to fall into?"

"Because I'm truly beat, man. Kerouacked. Like whooo! That's how come I can't make lunch."

"Affair of the heart?"

"Mostly the back. We got this new dark-haired production assistant that just came on the show day before yesterday. One of these girls that carries a clipboard like it was Brando's shirt. And the minute our eyes clashed yesterday, I knew it was a thing. Clickarootie! So after the talk-down session yesterday afternoon I asked her out for a drink. Guess what she ordered! Some kind of Chablis, whatever the hell that is. I figured, Oh boy, a non-alcoholic, she's a basket-hanger, you ain't never going to get this chick boiled, Hank. So we're unlaxing, talking TV and Akiyoshi and Cannonball Adderley—she was to the Newport thing, turns out—and sex and Zen—"

"And sex."

"And sex, and then all of a sudden she passes me on the curve. She's making these statements, way out. I mean this girl sounds real far out, *real* far out. So I'm heavy-footing, I'm talking bold and she's keeping up—very frank stuff, Paul—"

"Phil."

"Phil. Jesus, why did I make that slip? What's with me these days?"

"Ask your shrinker."

"Listen. Don't think I don't need it. I got the evidence. Anyway, the reason I'm not making it today is account of that chick. I'm supposed to show for the talk-down at five, but I don't know how the hell I'll make it. I'm a wreck. Listen, do I sound funny?"

"Rosen and Jacoby are funnier."

"I mean my speech. Because I got this swollen lip on one side makes me look like Cheetah. I put myself on a liquid-type diet."

"Your labials are a bit sluggish. But, like the announcers say, it's the bowels that express your personality."

"And I still got good vowel movement, thank God. Hey! Throw me a cover line, quick!"

" 'Thank you, mother.' 'I know there are people out there because I can hear you breathing.' 'I'll fire the s.o.b. that wrote that one.' "

"You should do our warm-ups. Your cover lines need cover lines."

"So what happened?"

"I'd tell you, Phil, but I know that cuddly operator of yours is listening in . . . Hi, peaches . . . OK (Did I hear a click?) . . . Anyway, we're relating, like the social workers say, and she's sober but talking *mucho grande* and I say all of a sudden, 'Do you dig Mitch? Because I got a great waxing of an oldie, *The Yellow Rose of Texas*, that should glom many spins turntable-wise.' "

"Do you honest to God talk like that to production assistants?"

"It's love-talk, man. Don't knock it. Shows them you think you're with it."

"What's she look like?"

"Well, she's healthy enough upstairs, but she wouldn't knock you out face-wise. Cute little roll when she walks—an occupational thing, I guess. But the main thing is she has these real bear rug eyes that she could be reciting Edgar A. Guest and you would still communicate."

"So then?"

"So I say, 'How about hearing it?' She says, 'OK, when?' Is she bluffing? I say, 'How about like now?' 'No,' she says, 'I got to see about some props for the show. We're low on pastry.' And her pretty mouth opens in a chuckle. I figure, Uh-oh. A snow job. Two bucks' worth of Chablis down the drain and zero-zero. I guess my face showed it. Then she looks thoughtful and says, 'But how about like ten o'clockish?' Real hip, eh, Phil? So I give her my address and call off a thing with Manda. *Poker,* you know?"

"Which is Manda?"

"The off-off-Broadway one that thinks I'm going to marry her. You met her, remember? I mean, she practically bought the old shoes!"

"You could do a helluva lot worse, buddy."

"Man, I *lived* with this chick for two months. I know what domesticity with her would be like. All the time fights, listening to Stanislavsky, socks in the bathroom . . . Incidentally, you're a player, in case you get quizzed."

"Winner or loser?"

"Loser, a bill and a half. You're dying to pull even, in case I got to bust more dates. I won twenty, so these games shouldn't seem uneconomic."

"Your friend show up?"

"She showed up. A cuckoo! She broke every damn rule in the book! You know how every boy's ideal is to find a real presentable for-fun girl who you can play like a banjo? Well, this one you play like a missile. I mean the kind of missile that really goes off. With a very short countdown. I'd shaved and laid out the liquor—even a flagon of Chablis, because that's the kind of sport I am—when she knocks at five to ten. Her coat is hardly off when we're cozying on the couch watching TV and the hell with drinks or my Gleason album. The show is some kind of cowboy jazz and I'm pointing out boners, like the shadow falling on one side of the street one time and the other side the next time—this is better than *Songs of Solomon,* I've found out—and, well, I won't get clinical on account of little big-ears on your switchboard over there. But suffice to say she's got a very passable, pneumatic body and we're improvising like crazy, the furniture is crashing all around us, and the first thing I know my back is on fire—all over scratches —and she bit my lip so hard with her pretty little teeth I had to tell Irma I got into a fist-fight. All this action in about twelve minutes by the clock—before the middle commercial."

"Is the fight at the poker game?"

"No, at a bar. I'll carry the ball on this. It's safer . . . Man, I tell you, I am one gasping wreck after a couple hours' tussling.

Utterly done done. So finally the set is humming with no picture on the screen, it's three in the morning and I got to boot her the hell out of there. But this chick is stubborn as well as energetic. She lives in Newark. I'm bloody, I ache, but—she knows I got a car—she wants me to drive her to Newark! Either that or she stays, she says. You ever see a girl with no clothes on stick her chin out and act stubborn? A real scene. But I know if I drive her to Newark there'll be a smashup, sure. She'll attack me at the toll booth or inside the Lincoln Tunnel. The nails on this cuckoo! Finally, by acting tough, I convince her I got a very finicky (finicky!) roommate that works nights at a nightclub and it's really his pad, so I got to be on my good behavior. So she finally gets dressed, burned up, and goes. I just have time to pick up the furniture and put ointment on my back, as much as I can reach, and put on thick pajamas so the grooves don't show through, when Irma staggers in. She's pretty loaded, but still rational. But she's tired, thank God, so she just waves in a friendly way and flops into the sack.

"I got no more trouble for the rest of the night, except that I have to lie on my stomach and the pain in my back is killing me so much I can't sleep. Who needs it? I kept asking myself. In the morning when she got up she sees me lying there like a cover for *Rugged Adventure,* hoping the blood don't show. It didn't and she swallowed the story how I got my lip and waggled off to work. So that there is why—between loss of epidermis, sunk eyes and big lip—I'm not eating in public. End of tale. I'm doing my schlong stuff for the show right here."

"Well, listen, Hank. You want to make it tomorrow? I'm free and there's this script we think needs doctoring and it might mean an interesting piece of change for you."

"I can't, Phil. Listen. Can you mail it? Along with whatever other poop there is on it? Because I may not be able to make it tomorrow, either."

"Hell, you'll be healed by then."

"I kind of doubt it. Because the chick is coming back tonight."

"Lock the door. Anyway, how do you know she's coming back?"

"Because I phoned and asked her."

"Oh."

"Yeah . . . Well, so long, Phil."

"So long, Hank. I'll mail that thing."

"Crazy. Sorry I couldn't make it. But I'm really beat."

"OK. 'Bye."

"Mr. Forrest? While you were on the phone, a Mr. Baker of Judson, Pierce and Finch called. Hilltop 9-5000. He'd like you to call back. No message. And the photos from Famco just came. Shall I have them sent in, sir?"

"If you would, Marilyn."

"And one other thing, Mr. Forrest. Will you be going out to lunch at one?"

"Yes, but it'll be a quickie."

"Uh, one more thing, sir."

"Yes?"

"While I was waiting to see if you were through on the phone so I could switch Mr. Baker to your line, I happened to overhear you were going to mail some kind of package over to Mr., uh, Bullett. Now, I could drop it off during my lunch hour today and it would, uh, arrive that much sooner."

"Well, isn't that pretty inconvenient for you, Marilyn? His apartment's in the sixties, and I might not have it ready till about two-thirty."

"That's all right, sir. I'll wait."

MADDENED BY MYSTERY: OR, THE DEFECTIVE DETECTIVE

✒ STEPHEN LEACOCK

The Great Detective sat in his office.

He wore a long green gown and half a dozen secret badges pinned to the outside of it.

Three or four pairs of false whiskers hung on a whisker-stand beside him.

Goggles, blue spectacles and motor glasses lay within easy reach.

He could completely disguise himself at a second's notice.

Half a bucket of cocaine and a dipper stood on a chair at his elbow.

His face was absolutely impenetrable.

A pile of cryptograms lay on the desk. The Great Detective hastily tore them open one after the other, solved them, and threw them down the cryptogram-chute at his side.

There was a rap at the door.

The Great Detective hurriedly wrapped himself in a pink coat, adjusted a pair of false black whiskers and cried,

"Come in."

His secretary entered. "Ha," said the detective, "it is you!"

He laid aside his disguise.

"Sir," said the young man in intense excitement, "a mystery has been committed!"

"Ha!" said the Great Detective, his eye kindling, "is it such as to completely baffle the police of the entire continent?"

"They are so completely baffled with it," said the secretary, "that they are lying collapsed in heaps; many of them have committed suicide."

"So," said the detective, "and is the mystery one that is absolutely unparalleled in the whole recorded annals of the London police?"

"It is."

"And I suppose," said the detective, "that it involves names which you would scarcely dare to breathe, at least without first using some kind of atomiser or throat-gargle."

"Exactly."

"And it is connected, I presume, with the highest diplomatic consequences, so that if we fail to solve it England will be at war with the whole world in sixteen minutes?"

His secretary, still quivering with excitement, again answered yes.

"And finally," said the Great Detective, "I presume that it was committed in broad daylight, in some such place as the entrance to the Bank of England, or in the cloak-room of the House of Commons, and under the very eyes of the police?"

"Those," said the secretary, "are the very conditions of the mystery."

"Good," said the Great Detective, "now wrap yourself in this disguise, put on these brown whiskers and tell me what it is."

The secretary wrapped himself in a blue domino with lace insertions, then, bending over, he whispered in the ear of the Great Detective:

"The Prince of Wurttemberg has been kidnapped."

The Great Detective bounded from his chair as if he had been kicked from below.

A prince stolen! Evidently a Bourbon! The scion of one of the oldest families in Europe kidnapped. Here was a mystery indeed worthy of his analytical brain.

His mind began to move like lightning.

"Stop!" he said, "how do you know this?"

The secretary handed him a telegram. It was from the Prefect of Police of Paris. It read: "The Prince of Wurttemberg stolen. Probably forwarded to London. Must have him here for the opening day of Exhibition. £ 1,000 reward."

So! The Prince had been kidnapped out of Paris at the very time when his appearance at the International Exposition would have been a political event of the first magnitude.

With the Great Detective to think was to act, and to act was to think. Frequently he could do both together.

"Wire to Paris for a description of the Prince."

The secretary bowed and left.

At the same moment there was slight scratching at the door.

A visitor entered. He crawled stealthily on his hands and knees. A hearthrug thrown over his head and shoulders disguised his identity.

He crawled to the middle of the room.

Then he rose.

Great Heaven!

It was the Prime Minister of England.

"You!" said the detective.

"Me," said the Prime Minister.

"You have come in regard to the kidnapping of the Prince of Wurttemberg?"

The Prime Minister started.

"How do you know?" he said.

The Great Detective smiled his inscrutable smile.

"Yes," said the Prime Minister. "I will use no concealment. I am interested, deeply interested. Find the Prince of Wurttemberg, get him safe back to Paris and I will add £500 to the reward already offered. But listen," he said impressively as he left the room, "see to it that no attempt is made to alter the marking of the prince, or to clip his tail."

So! To clip the Prince's tail! The brain of the Great Detective reeled. So! a gang of miscreants had conspired to—but no! the thing was not possible.

There was another rap at the door.

A second visitor was seen. He wormed his way in, lying almost prone upon his stomach, and wriggling across the floor. He was enveloped in a long purple cloak. He stood up and peeped over the top of it.

Great Heaven!

It was the Archbishop of Canterbury!

"Your Grace!" exclaimed the detective in amazement—"pray do not stand, I beg you. Sit down, lie down, anything rather than stand."

The Archbishop took off his mitre and laid it wearily on the whisker-stand.

"You are here in regard to the Prince of Wurttemberg."

The Archbishop started and crossed himself. Was the man a magician?

"Yes," he said, "much depends on getting him back. But I have only come to say this: my sister is desirous of seeing you. She is coming here. She has been extremely indiscreet and her fortune hangs upon the Prince. Get him back to Paris or I fear she will be ruined."

The Archbishop regained his mitre, uncrossed himself, wrapped his cloak about him, and crawled stealthily out on his hands and knees, purring like a cat.

The face of the Great Detective showed the most profound sympathy. It ran up and down in furrows. "So," he muttered, "the sister of the Archbishop, the Countess of Dasleigh!" Accustomed as he was to the life of the aristocracy, even the Great Detective felt that there was here intrigue of more than customary complexity.

There was a loud rapping at the door.

There entered the Countess of Dashleigh. She was all in furs.

She was the most beautiful woman in England. She strode imperiously into the room. She seized a chair imperiously and seated herself on it, imperial side up.

She took off her tiara of diamonds and put it on the tiara-holder beside her and uncoiled her boa of pearls and put it on the pearl-stand.

"You have come," said the Great Detective, "about the Prince of Wurttemberg."

"Wretched little pup!" said the Countess of Dashleigh in disgust.

So! A further complication! Far from being in love with the Prince, the Countess denounced the young Bourbon as a pup!

"You are interested in him, I believe."

"Interested!" said the Countess. "I should rather say so. Why, I bred him!"

"You which?" gasped the Great Detective, his usually impassive features suffused with a carmine blush.

"I bred him," said the Countess, "and I've got £10,000 upon his chances, so no wonder I want him back in Paris. Only listen," she said, "if they've got hold of the Prince and cut his tail or spoiled the markings of his stomach it would be far better to have him quietly put out of the way here."

The Great Detective reeled and leaned up against the side of the room. So! The cold-blooded admission of the beautiful woman for the moment took away his breath! Herself the mother of the young Bourbon, misallied with one of the greatest families of Europe, staking her fortune on a Royalist plot, and yet with so instinctive a knowledge of European politics as to know that any removal of the hereditary birth-marks of the Prince would forfeit for him the sympathy of the French populace.

The Countess resumed her tiara.

She left.

The secretary re-entered.

"I have three telegrams from Paris," he said, "they are completely baffling."

He handed over the first telegram.

It read:

"The Prince of Wurttemberg has a long, wet snout, broad ears, very long body, and short hind legs."

The Great Detective looked puzzled.

He read the second telegram.

"The Prince of Wurttemberg is easily recognised by his deep bark."

And then the third.

"The Prince of Wurttemberg can be recognised by the patch of white hair across the centre of his back."

The two men looked at one another. The mystery was maddening, impenetrable.

The Great Detective spoke.

"Give me my coat," he said. "These clues must be followed up," then pausing, while his quick brain analysed and summed up the evidence before him—"a young man," he muttered, "evidently young since described as a 'pup,' with a long, wet snout (ha! addicted obviously to drinking), a streak of white hair across his back (a first sign of the results of abandoned life)—yes, yes," he continued, "with this clue I shall find him easily."

The Great Detective rose.

He wrapped himself in a long black cloak with white whiskers and blue spectacles attached.

Completely disguised, he issued forth.

He began the search.

For four days he visited every corner of London.

He entered every saloon in the city. In each of them he drank a glass of rum. In some of them he assumed the disguise of a sailor. In others he entered as a soldier. Into others he penetrated as a clergyman. His disguise was perfect. Nobody paid any attention to him as long as he had the price of a drink.

The search proved fruitless.

Two young men were arrested under suspicion of being the Prince, only to be released.

The identification was incomplete in each case.

One had a long wet snout but no hair on his back.

The other had hair on his back but couldn't bark.

Neither of them was the young Bourbon.

The Great Detective continued his search.

He stopped at nothing.

Secretly, after nightfall, he visited the home of the Prime Minister. He examined it from top to bottom. He measured all the doors and windows. He took up the flooring. He inspected the plumbing. He examined the furniture. He found nothing.

With equal secrecy he penetrated into the palace of the Archbishop. He examined it from top to bottom. Disguised as a choirboy he took part in the offices of the church. He found nothing.

Still undismayed, the Great Detective made his way into the home of the Countess of Dashleigh. Disguised as a housemaid, he entered the service of the Countess.

Then at last the clue came which gave him a solution of the mystery.

On the wall of the Countess' boudoir was a large framed engraving.

It was a portrait.

Under it was a printed legend:

THE PRINCE OF WURTTEMBERG

The portrait was that of a Dachshund.

The long body, the broad ears, the unclipped tail, the short hind legs—all was there.

In the fraction of a second the lightning mind of the Great Detective had penetrated the whole mystery.

THE PRINCE WAS A DOG! ! ! !

Hastily throwing a coat over his housemaid's dress, he rushed to the street. He summoned a passing hansom, and in a few moments was at his house.

"I have it," he gasped to his secretary, "the mystery is solved. I have pieced it together. By sheer analysis I have reasoned it out. Listen—hind legs, hair on back, wet snout, pup—eh, what? does that suggest nothing to you?"

"Nothing," said the secretary; "it seems perfectly hopeless."

The Great Detective, now recovered from his excitement, smiled faintly.

"It means simply this, my dear fellow. The Prince of Wurttemberg is a dog, a prize Dachshund. The Countess of Dashleigh bred him, and he is worth some £25,000 in addition to the prize of £10,000 offered at the Paris dog show. Can you wonder that—"

At that moment the Great Detective was interrupted by the scream of a woman.

"Great Heaven!"

The Countess of Dashleigh dashed into the room.

Her face was wild.

Her tiara was in disorder.

Her pearls were dripping all over the place.

She wrung her hands and moaned.

"They have cut his tail," she gasped, "and taken all the hair off his back. What can I do? I am undone! !"

"Madame," said the Great Detective, calm as bronze, "do yourself up. I can save you yet."

"You!"

"Me!"

"How?"

"Listen. This is how. The Prince was to have been shown at Paris."

The Countess nodded.

"Your fortune was staked on him?"

The Countess nodded again.

"The dog was stolen, carried to London, his tail cut and his marks disfigured."

Amazed at the quiet penetration of the Great Dectective, the Countess kept on nodding and nodding.

"And you are ruined?"

"I am," she gasped, and sank down on the floor in a heap of pearls.

"Madame," said the Great Detective, "all is not lost."

He straightened himself up to his full height. A look of inflexibility flickered over his features.

The honour of England, the fortune of the most beautiful woman in England was at stake.

"I will do it," he murmured.

"Rise, dear lady," he continued. "Fear nothing. I WILL IMPERSONATE THE DOG! ! !'"

That night the Great Detective might have been seen on the deck of the Calais packet boat with his secretary. He was on his hands and knees in a long black cloak, and his secretary had him on a short chain.

He barked at the waves exultingly and licked the secretary's hand.

"What a beautiful dog," said the passengers.

The disguise was absolutely complete.

The Great Detective had been coated over with mucilage to which dog hairs had been applied. The markings on his back were perfect. His tail, adjusted with an automatic coupler, moved up and down responsive to every thought. His deep eyes were full of intelligence.

Next day he was exhibited in the Dachshund class at the International show.

He won all hearts.

"*Quel beau chien!*" cried the French people.

"*Ach! was ein Dog!*" cried the Spanish.

The Great Detective took the first prize!

The fortune of the Countess was saved.

Unfortunately as the Great Detective had neglected to pay the dog tax, he was caught and destroyed by the dog-catchers. But that is, of course, quite outside of the present narrative, and is only mentioned as an odd fact in conclusion.

MAN HERE KEEPS GETTING ARRESTED ALL THE TIME

✍ JOHN MC NULTY

Grogan got arrested again Thursday. Talking in this place on Third Avenue Friday night, he said he was getting sick and tired of it. That's about the ninth time he got arrested lately. He seems to be having a streak.

Grogan is a nice, quiet little man. He bets on race horses and thinks about them night and day. Mostly he gets arrested in raids on puny horse rooms around Third, Second Avenue, occasionally Lexington Avenue.

Grogan's a solemn, small, scientific-minded little man, with no laughs at all written on his dead pan. He comes by being scientific-minded honestly, because in Ireland his old man was a Latin scholar just for fun. That's how Grogan got his middle name, which is Vercingetorix. His whole name is Malachy Vercingetorix Grogan, but they call him Grogan the Horseplayer. It sounds like a trade, like bricklaying.

Getting arrested doesn't bother Grogan in his pride or leave any marks on his character. He manages to remain altogther aloof from the cops that arrest him. But what gets him sore is he says you miss your dinner when you get arrested in these raids. They almost always happen half past four in the afternoon and no Night Court to stick you in front of until about ten o'clock that night.

"I don't know do they folly me around or what, those plain-clothes policemen," Grogan said. "But it seems lately no sooner am I settled down nice and busy in one of these horse rooms than along about the fifth race at Aqueduct in come the policemen again.

"They're decent enough when they come in on a raid, unless

166

once in a while somebody in the crowd of horseplayers shows signs getting tough. They have to paste them a couple then—not too hard—so everybody else will get the idea what's done is done and make the best of it and they'll know it's a raid. These couple of pastes in the jaw for somebody is what they might call in a show establishing a mood. The policemen establishes a mood that way."

This last arrest, Grogan said, just about broke the back on his camel. He got to brooding about it. Paddy Ferrarty, the night bartender, often says about Grogan, "He's Irish and he broods easy."

"It's heartbreaking the way I got to do now," Grogan went on. "They got me half scared of the little horse rooms, and I don't ketch holt of enough money for decent poolrooms. I usually got seven dollars, only, to start with. Consequence is I'm playing with guys makes book in an auto on a corner. They sit in the auto and won't let me or the other horseplayers sit in it, naturally—ain't room enough.

"No, we got to stand in the rain or doorways to look at the *Racing Form,* and walk over to the auto and make bets, or get the results that comes in over the radio. You seen that kind of book-making.

"This last raid—I don't know, it got tiresome. I make out better than the other guys arrested. I'm used to it. Like when they're going to lead you out to the patrol wagon at the curb, nobody wants to be first outside the door and pass through the crowd. A crowd always stands around as close as they can to a patrol wagon, and the cops make a space between 'em, like an aisle outside a church for a wedding.

"But I got over all that bashfulness about going out first and let the crowd gape at you. The hell with them in the crowd. You're not criminals anyway, only horseplayers meaning no harm, only want to win a couple dollars. And what the hell, the cops themselves ain't even mad at you; they got to make a couple raids every week to put in the records.

"And what I found out is you get across the sidewalk first and into the wagon and you get a seat. Why, the last time they had twenty-seven guys jammed in there, standing up, sitting on each other, piled up every which way, miserable. So I'm first across the sidewalk—let them gape—and I got a seat.

"First they took us in this last raid down to the police station on East Thirty-fifth Street. The whole twenty-seven in a big room and certainly a mixed-up bunch. They had guys like me, and some Longchamps waiters with red braids on their coats would probably get fired because it was five o'clock by then and they ought to be back to work. Three or four horseplayers had helmets on. Steel helmets. These helmet guys work in the slaughterhouse on First Avenyuh. They got to wear helmets because the big sides of beefs run along a conveyor on hooks and without the beefs the bare hooks sometimes hits the guys in the head. Therefore helmets.

"The way you mill around in that police station is an awful waste of time. Just mope there, but a guy sells coffee if you want it. That helps and he makes a handy dollar with all the prisoners dumped in there all the time.

"It's about six o'clock before they took us up to East Sixty-seventh Street, what they call Division Headquarters. They count you before they put you in the wagon and they count you up at East Sixty-seventh Street and they count you before they take you out of there. My God, you get sick of being counted! I hate cops counting me, but they have a slip says twenty-seven guys arrested and they deliver them around from station to station like merchandise. Another thing that's not becomin' at all is that in East Sixty-seventh they put you in cells. No matter who you are, getting put in a cell can make you sad, even if only for horseplaying. There's something about seeing a man walk loose by the door and you can't walk loose but got to look through bars that sinks your heart out if you let it. Only I don't let it. The thing that bothers me is why do they go through all this at all, to say nothing of making you miss your dinner? Why do they keep bothering poor, simple, ordinary horseplayers and turn them loose anyway in the finish, which they always do?

"It seems useless to me. I always thought now for years I love to study horses and bet them when I can because it is one thing you can do by yourself and harms nobody at all. I can be busy with horses, the *Racing Form* or maybe the *Morning Telegraph,* all winter nights and summer nights in Bickford's or in my room and never harm anybody, but they got to keep on arresting us. Getting married causes trouble, drinking causes trouble, working wears a man out, and I see guys all around me dying making successes out of themselves. Why can't they let me harm nobody just studying horses and playing 'em when I can?

"I almost forgot to say just before the raid I bet a horse at Suffolk, two dollars win, with Louie the bookie. But then the raid come, and of course they stopped the radio, gathered up all the *Forms* and all, and with all the moving from station to station I couldn't find out how the Suffolk race come out. None of the cops were watching me especially in the raid, and I snuck an Arlington Park part of the *Form* into my sock, folded up, and I had that at East Sixty-seventh Street. I could study that in the cell, and they run late out there at Arlington because it's in Chicago. Well, damn if I didn't find a horse in the last race out there I'd been watching for weeks. He could win easy, and luck would have it Louie walk by the cell and stopped there. He must have slipped a cop something and they broke him out of a cell and let him walk in the corridor back and forth—more comforting than in a cell. I asked Louie if he would let me bet the last at Arlington, although by that time the race was over. I didn't have money, but if the Suffolk horse had win, well, I could 'if' some money off him. That means if the first horse wins, you can bet some of the win on another one. It's like a contingency basis in the legal world, only it's 'iffing' in horse rooms. 'Honest to God, don't you know how the race come out at Arlington?' Louie asked me. 'Nobody told you, did they, in jail here?' I told him honest to God I didn't know. 'O.K.' he says. 'You're an honest guy, Grogan. You can have four win on the Arlington horse.' Then he walked away from the cell. They both win, it later turn out, and so I beat Louie for sixteen-seventy.

"I was glad I went out first to the wagon when they moved us to Night Court over on West Fifty-fourth Street. I tell you why.

"It was dark when they moved us, and of course the wagon was jammed up again. The seat I got was up front, and there's a round hole in the partition that divides the driver off from us. Well, as we drove along I could look through that round hole and see all the corners I knew. It was very interesting, just looking through that hole and seeing a particular building and figuring out 'This is Lexington and Sixty-fourth' or else 'This is Lex and Fifty-ninth.'

"Of course, they counted us again at the Night Court, where you stand around in a detention pen. I felt like saying, 'Stop counting me. I'm still one guy, the same as I been all my life.' But what's the use? The less said in a detention pen the better.

"The bailiff got me a little mad. They haul you up in a bunch before the magistrate, and when it came our turn, the bunch from our particular raid, what do you suppose the bailiff shouted to the magistrate? Well, he hollered, 'Malachy V. Grogan and twenty-six others!' I asked him, 'What's the idea singlin' me out?' 'Aw, you're here all the time,' he says. I let it go at that.

"They dismissed us, the magistrate did, the way he always does. We get charged with dis. con., they call it, means disorderly conduct, and there's a couple minutes' blather and they turn us loose, ten o'clock or so and no dinner yet. They hold Louie. They got him charged with main. nuis., which is maintaining a nuisance, probably meaning Malachy V. Grogan and twenty-six others. It all seems useless, and I don't know why they got to keep arresting us all, not doing anybody a bit of harm but finding an interesting way to put in all the days and nights.

"Louie give me the sixteen-seventy after we got out. He got out. He got bailed in no time. I knew he would because Louie's the kind nobody pens him up very long and so I was waiting in Fifty-fourth when he come out. He bought a *Telegraph* at the stand there at Fiftieth and Broadway and we found out how the races we missed in jail come out."

HOW TO PLAY COMPANY POLITICS

ᴇᴏ SHEPHERD MEAD

It goes without saying that you, as a rising young man, will live a clean life, rise early, work hard, and keep your employer's interests at heart.

These are all laudable traits, but of course they will get you nowhere without a thorough understanding of company politics.

Company politics should never be confused with national politics or political parties, though it is safe to assume that if you expect to rise rapidly to the top you will either *be* a Republican or *seem* to be one.

Be a politician

Do not confuse this with being a politician in the ward politics sense. Businesses are governed, not by the majority, but by the men at the top, in a manner reminiscent of the medieval Italian city-state. Read Machiavelli—and then learn the following easy rules:

1. *Pick the Right Team.* In your company, as in all healthy, live-wire groups, there are bound to be areas of friction. Enter them with a will.

There are always two or more factions fighting for control, or for favor with the Big Wheels. It is essential to maintain strict neutrality long enough to determine which side is going to win.

No matter how well you do your work, if you choose the wrong side you will soon be in a sorry plight indeed.

2. *Be a Pussyfooter.* During this wait-and-see period others may try to force you to choose sides. Resist them!

For example, during a heated argument at a meeting you may be asked:

"Well, Finch, what do *you* think about it?"

The chips would seem to be plainly down, but a skillful pussy-footer need not be dismayed.

"Oh, it's obvious, sir!" (*Never* seem *to pussyfoot!*) "Mr. Blank's statement is so clear—" (*A smile here to Blank, who may still be in the running.*) "—that I would say by all means buy more wickets! On the other hand, Mr. Threep's point is certainly well taken!" (*Threep is far from being counted out, and you know his mother-in-law holds a big batch of stock.*) "I'd say buy sump pumps, too!"

In short, steer a bold path, right down the middle. After the meeting it is well to see both Blank and Threep, separately.

"Hope I didn't let you down, sir. Hated to hurt poor old Threep's (Blank's) feelings. Wouldn't want to kick a man who's going down!"

3. *Make Your Move.* After it is clear that Threep, say, *is* going down, the humane thing to do is to finish him off as quickly as possible. Attack him freely, and preferably in Blank's presence.

"Threep's point is well taken," you say, with a condescending smile, "if we assume his information is correct. However, it looks to me as though he has been badly misguided." (*You pity the poor old devil, discredit his whole team, yet maintain an attitude of great magnanimity.*) "In line with Mr. Blank's figures, it would be disastrous to follow Threep's recommendations. Buy wickets, buy *more* wickets, and drop the whole sump pump line!"

If you administer the *coup de grâce* to Threep, Blank will soon make you his right-hand man. You are on your way up—well deserved reward for courage and clear thinking.

From this point on, follow Blank loyally. There is nothing like loyalty, as long as your man moves up fast enough to leave plenty of room behind.

If he does not, never fear. You must think first of the company's good, and if Blank is not Doing His Job, you must not let sentiment interfere. By this time you should be skillful at giving people the business. Give it to Blank, in a nice way, and afterwards do your best to find him another job. He will thank you for it. Care for your friends, and they will care for you.

4. *Stab the Right Backs.* Your manner at all times should be friendly, kind, and courteous. The good businessman is everyone's Pal.

But from time to time some selfish person will stand in your way.

Before dispatching him it is well to ask yourself: Is he married to the boss's daughter? Is he a fair-haired boy? Is he related to a customer or client?

If he has attained his position because of ability, a few disparaging remarks *in the right ears* will do for him quickly—but beware the man who has deeper roots!

5. *Guard Your Own Back.* You can assume that your assistants will serve you loyally and selflessly, as long as you keep your distance.

But the wise businessman always protects his rear. The surest way of doing this is to be careful in choosing assistants. It can be done in several different ways. Let us examine them all.

a. *The Happy-Moron Theory.* Your safest course is to hire only imbeciles as assistants. They will worship you—as assistants should!—and will never be able to threaten your position. If you are a good talker you should be able to convince management that they are doing a grand job, but only because they have you for guidance.

b. *The Divide-and-Conquer Theory.* This is no course for timid souls. Hire the best men—but make them compete for your favor. You will find it an easy task to poison their little minds and turn them against each other—but in a constructive way. Make sure you are always the Great White Father to whom they will run in peril.

c. *The Ugly-Duckling Theory.* One chap with extremely modest ability and a glib tongue rose rapidly to the top by this method. He hired brilliant but unpresentable assistants, men with fine minds but repulsive personalities who sat behind filing cabinets doing superb work for which he took full credit.

Few would have had the courage to take so daring a step!

But you may find a fourth and even better way. At this moment experiments are going on in offices throughout our nation.

6. *Upward and Onward.* Clearly the best way, however, to keep ahead of your assistants is to blaze a bold, straight path—forward! As you move rapidly ahead with giant strides your assistants will have enough to do filling the posts you leave behind. You will be an inspiration to those under you. It is only those ahead who need beware!

7. *Choose the Right Wife.* Remember, the American home is sacred, and it is a shoddy fellow indeed who uses his wife to further his own selfish ends.

However, if you live in a small city or company town it is well to choose your wife carefully, as she, too, will have to play her part. Otherwise you may be forced to replace her, and this should *not* be done frequently, and then *only between jobs.*

Choose a wife who is adaptable and flexible, who will fit in well with the group. She should not, of course, have any definite opinions, or any special mentality, as these will soon rub others the wrong way. It is important above all not to offend.

A college education is of great value to the company wife as long as she is careful not to let it creep into her conversation or influence her reading. The social graces, skill at cards, and ability to dress well, all these real tangible attributes of the college graduate, will stand her in good stead.

Most important is to find a girl whom the influential wives will admire. She must be a good clean-cut American girl, ready to make many sacrifices to endear herself to the women around her.

She must be prepared to perform a few simple services:

> "Couldn't we pick up your little dears in the morning? After all, I'm *used* to getting up at six!"

Or:

> "I'm so glad you admire Hilda's cooking. Ponty was wondering if you wouldn't like to *have* her."

And remember, soon the shoe will be on the other foot. As you rise in prestige and authority she will have *her* innings—if you're still willing to put up with her.

8. *Pick the Right Suburb.* If your job is in a very large metropolitan area, it is most important to choose the right suburb.

Remember, it is almost as easy to go from New York to Chicago as it is to go from Upper Hohokus, New Jersey, to East Squague, Long Island. This is an advantage. Use it! It will insulate you from those who might annoy you, and put you right into the laps of those with whom you would like to be cozy.

Beware the Commuter's Bridge Game. It is a rare man indeed who remains long on speaking terms with his "cronies" of the morning and evening bridge game. If you *must* play bridge, choose men in another company, preferably another industry. Some men are slow to forgive, and smoldering hatreds have blasted many a budding career.

Be a Nodder. The skillful Paper Reader (as opposed to the Bridge Commuter) soon learns to give influential acquaintances a warm, charming nod-and-smile as he passes their half-empty seats and sits *with a total stranger.*

This is to be recommended even if the acquaintance is important to you in company politics. It may seem a wasted opportunity, but it may prevent your being transferred abruptly to North Dakota.

9. *Pick the Right Country Club.* This, of course, is a *must.* The gay man-to-man *Gemütlichkeit* of the locker room, the rough-and-ready camaraderie of sand trap and water hole will stand you in good stead in the hurly-burly of the business world.

One keen young man made a smashing success by always managing to arrive first at his boss's ball when it lay in the rough. After deftly kicking it out of a rabbit hole he would say:

"Here it is, J.B., in the clear!"

"Good boy, Finch. Mighty lucky I'm not in that damned rabbit hole!"

"Yes, sir, mighty lucky!"

"Matter of fact, I always seem to have better luck when I go around with you, Finch!"

IMPRESARIO ON THE LAM

✑ S. J. PERELMAN

The voice that came over the wire last Thursday was full of gravel
and Hollywood subjunctives. It was a voice trained to cut through
the din of night clubs and theater rehearsals, a flexible instrument
that could shift from adulation to abuse in a syllable, ingratiating
yet peremptory, a rich syrup of unction and specious authority.
"Listen, Clyde, you don't know me from a hole in the ground," it
began with deadly accuracy, "but I'm the agent for a friend of
yours, Morris Flesh." Before I could disavow ever having heard of
Flesh, his representative had washed his hands of him and was
scuttling down the fairway. "I've got a client deeply interested in
putting on a revue," he confided. "A smart, intimate show that
kids the passing scene, the various fads and foibles like television
and mah-jongg and psychoanalysis—dig me? Morris recommends
you to pen the sketches, and while I personally would rather have
a name, I'm willing to gamble on his opinion. Now, here's the
score, Pops. My backer is strictly from Dixie, a peasant from the
tall rhubarbs. I'm running the creative side and this is what I have
in mind." I laid the receiver gently on the desk and went out to
lunch. When I returned two hours later, the monologue was
purling on as inexorably as the Blue Nile. "This girl composer has
got Vassar in an uproar, baby," the voice was affirming. "She's the
hottest thing that ever hit Poughkeepsie—another Cole Porter,
only younger. Sophisticated but simple at the same time." I hung
up, and dialing the business office, vanished into the limbo of un-
listed telephone subscribers.

Though not constitutionally averse to the crackle of greenbacks,
I learned many years ago—twenty-eight, in fact—that of all the
roads to insolvency open to my profession, entanglement in a revue is the shortest. Every revue since *The Garrick Gaieties* has

been hatched from the same larva, an impassioned declaration by some seer flushed with Martinis that what Broadway needs this season is a smart, intimate show like *The Garrick Gaieties*. In 1932, Poultney Kerr, a onetime yacht broker riding out the depression on a cask of brandy, said it with such persistence that a group of idealists gave him a hundred thousand dollars to demonstrate, and he did so with a *cauchemar* called *Sherry Flip*. Kerr's qualifications as a producer, apart from a honeyed tongue, were minimal. His executive ability was pitiful, his judgment paltry, and his equilibrium unstable in crisis. He did, nevertheless, look the big wheel—a corpulent, natty man given to Homburg hats and carnations in the buttonhole, with the classic empurpled nose of the *bon vivant* and a talent for imbibing oceans of Courvoisier without crumpling. I met him at a low ebb in my fortunes and left him at a lower. In between, I got so concentrated a dose of hysteria and wormwood that I still quail at the mention of sherry.

At a moment when my wallet was at its flabbiest, the project started in the classic tradition with an urgent phone call from Lytton Swazey, a lyric writer I had known casually around the doughnut shop in Times Square we both frequented. Could I, he asked, confer with him and his composer that afternoon at Kerr's apartment about an upcoming revue patterned after *The Garrick Gaieties?* I blacked my shoes in a flash and pelted over. The portents seemed dazzling. Swazey, after years of grinding out special material for willowy chanteuses in cocktail bars, had recently teamed up with a Russian composer named Herman Earl. Together they had confected a valiseful of show tunes, and it was on these, plus the half-dozen sketches I would supply, that *Sherry Flip* was to be based.

It may have been wishful thinking that warped my perspective, or a greenhorn's superstitious awe of song writers as demigods, but Swazey had hardly bawled out a couple of ballads before I put down my glass and emotionally announced, "Gentlemen, count me in." Needless to say, our sponsor was not outraged by my quick assent. He plied me with flattery and cognac, hailed me as a theatrical sibyl rivaling Daniel Frohman. The few tentative ideas for sketches I broached evoked paroxysms of laughter. "I don't want to put a jinx on it, boys," exulted Kerr, wrenching the cork from a fresh bottle of Hennessey, "but I think we've got a hit." What with all the self-congratulation and the mirage of fat royalties he conjured up, I agreed to terms that even a Mexican migrant worker would have flouted, and bowled off straightaway to Bachrach to be photographed. I figured I might not have the leisure to sit for him later when I became the toast of Broadway.

Lodged in an airless cubicle in Kerr's offices, I spent the next five weeks chewing licorice fortified with Benzedrine and evolving skits, emerging only to replenish myself with corned-beef sandwiches. *Sherry Flip*, meanwhile, was subtly changing from a collection of grandiose phrases into a living organism. A director, scenic designer, and choreographer materialized; the anteroom boiled with singers and dancers, tumblers and ventriloquists, sister acts and precocious children. Kerr himself preserved a state of Olympian detachment for the most part, huddling with lawyers in his sanctum. There were disquieting whispers that our finances were shaky, but as rehearsal day neared, he secured additional pledges, sounds of wassail again rang through the corridors, and we began on a note of the most buoyant optimism.

Rehearsals went swimmingly the first fortnight. Not a speck of artistic temperament marked the cast; everyone was bewitched by the vivacity of the score and the brilliance of the sketches. Manners were impeccable, the atmosphere as sunny as a Monet picnic. The, abruptly, the lid blew off. Halfway through her big solo one afternoon, our prima donna developed an acute attack of paranoia. Derogating the number as an inept Russian plagiarism of "Rio Rita," she declared that she would never sully her reputation by singing it in public. The composer, justifiably stung to fury, flew into a storm of picturesque Muscovite cuss-words. He offered to punch her nose—which, he added parenthetically, was bobbed—and threatened to bring her up before Equity on charges. The director patched up a shaky truce, but the incident had abraded the company's nerves and opened the door to further insubordination. Mysterious excrescences began to appear on the material I had furnished the actors. A diplomatic travesty of mine suddenly blossomed out with a routine in which, using a wallet stuffed with toilet paper, our top banana flimflammed a Polish butcher from Scranton. When I complained, I was told that it had scored a triumph on every burlesque wheel in America. If it offended Percy Bysshe Shelley—as he jocosely referred to me—I could return to writing for the little magazines. The barometer, in short, was falling, there were mutterings in the fo'c'sl, and one didn't have to be Ziegfeld to prophesy that *Sherry Flip* was in for many a squall before it reached port.

By the week prior to the Boston tryout, stilettos were flashing in earnest and the company buzzed like a hive of bees. The comedians, made overweening by victory, had woven a crazy quilt of drolleries and *double-entendres* that made the brain reel. They impersonated androgynes and humorous tramps, thwacked the showgirls' bottoms with rolled-up newspapers, and squirted water from their boutonnieres. Their improvisations totally unnerved Wigmore, the director, an able man around an Ibsen revival but a newcomer to the musical theater. The poor man fluttered about in a continual wax, wringing his hands like ZaSu Pitts and trying to assert his authority. In the dance department, there was a similar lack of co-ordination. The production numbers, two portentous ballets in the style colloquially known as "Fire in a Whorehouse," were being revised from day to day. Muscle-bound youths stamped about bearing dryads who whinnied in ecstasy; shoals of coryphees fled helter-skelter across the stage; and out on the apron, chin cupped in his hand, the choreographer brooded, dreaming up new flights of symbolism. To aggravate matters, a protegée of the composer's, a $55-dollar-a-week soprano with whom he had dallied in good faith, was loudly demanding a featured spot in the show, on pain of divulging the escapade to her husband. Whatever *Sherry Flip* lacked in smartness, its intimacy was unquestionable.

The *estocada*, however, was yet to come. Six o'clock of the evening before our departure for Boston, Murray Zweifel, the company manager, called me aside to retail alarming news—our producer had disappeared. Murray, a Broadway veteran, was on the verge of prostration. "He's quit the show," he said brokenly. "Walked out cold. We're done for." The particulars were simple enough, readily comprehensible to any student of alcohol. Kerr, unmanned by dissension with his backers and loath to open the show on what he contemptuously termed a shoestring, had taken refuge in the grape and abdicated. "The goddam fool is winging," Murray snuffled, grasping my lapels. "You've got to find him and get him on that train, baby. You're the only one who can do it—he won't listen to common sense."

The compliment was equivocal at best, and nine weeks of nightmare tension had taken their toll of me, but I realized that the welfare of sixty-odd folk was at stake, my own among theirs, and I knocked under. Pulling on a pair of waders, I set out to comb the bars that Kerr frequented. About ten-thirty, after a fruitless search of the West Side that extended to the clipjoints of Columbus Avenue, I flushed my man in a blind pig on East 54th Street. He was arm in arm with a prosperous Greek restaurateur from Bellows Falls; they had just consummated a deal to open a chain of diners in Thessaly and were toasting the venture in boilermakers. For all his carousing, Kerr was clear-eyed and crisp as muslin. He embraced me affectionately and insisted we pour a libation on the altar of friendship. The moment I disclosed my purpose, however, he grew violent. He was done with tinsel and sawdust, he declaimed; he wanted no more of the theater and its cutthroat machinations. I tried guile, supplication, and saccharine, but to no avail. Toward midnight, I phoned Zweifel for counsel.

"For crisake don't lose him!" he pleaded. "Feed him a Mickey—anything! If he's not on the nine o'clock to Boston, we're dead!"

"He's an iron man, Murray," I wailed. "He's mixing Scotch, vodka, bourbon—"

"Listen," he broke in. "Dr. Proctor's his physician—he'll cool him out with a sleeping powder! I'll phone him to expect you."

The process of extricating Kerr from the Greek took a full hour and the cunning of serpents. Eventually, though, I prevailed and, a trifle jingled from the soda I had taken in the line of duty, got him to the doctor's flat. A party was in progress, celebrating, I believe, Jenner's epochal discovery of the principle of vaccine, but not all the guests were medical. Out of the haze, I recall a tête-à-tête on a davenport with a blonde in salmon-pink satin, who read my palm and forecast business reverses. The augury cast a chill on our friendship, and moving off, I fell into a long, senseless wrangle about George Antheil with a musician resembling a carp. At intervals, Dr. Proctor's bibulous face swam into my field of vision, giving me conspiratorial winks and assuring me, in tones from outer space, that Kerr was under control. "Chloral hydrate," I heard him intone. "Just a few drops in his glass. He'll cave any time now." Hours later, I remember clinging to some portieres to steady myself while the doctor thickly conceded defeat. "Can't understand it," he said, laboring to focus his eyes. "Enough there to foal an ox. Average person go down like a felled ax. Got to hand it to old Poultney. Hard as nails." I groped past him to a book-lined alcove where Kerr was waltzing cheek to cheek with a cadaverous, sloe-eyed beauty on the order of Jetta Goudal. Now that drugs and entreaty had failed, my only recourse was insult. Castigating him for a yellow-belly and a welsher, I challenged him to redeem himself.

"I dare you to fly up to Boston!" I cried. "I've never been on a plane, but I'll do it if you will. That is," I said witheringly, "if you've got the moxie."

His brow darkened and he discarded the bush-league Eurasian with an oath. "We'll see who's got more moxie," he snarled. "Come along, you little four-eyed shrimp!"

I had won the first round; speeding through deserted streets toward the Newark Airport, my impresario's choler abated and he sank into a light coma. Instinct told me that if I could only lure him aboard the milk plane, his egotism would make him stick till the curtain rose. But Fate was dealing from the bottom of the deck. A dense, pea-soup fog blanketed the field, and the solitary clerk at the terminal held out little promise of improvement. The entire coast was closed in from Hatteras to the Bay of Fundy, he reported, savoring the despair on my face; even the mails were grounded. Kerr, meanwhile, had seized the opportunity to vanish into the washroom, where I found him draining a fifth of gin he had somehow managed to secrete in his clothes. There was only one hope now, to shanghai him back to the morning train; but with no taxi in sight and a bankroll of forty cents, it would obviously take some fancy logistics. Day was breaking when I finally wheedled the driver of a towel-supply truck into dropping us at the nearest subway stop. The ensuing ride into Manhattan unraveled what remained of my ganglia. In his sheltered life, Kerr, it appeared, had never ridden on a subway. He was seized with repugnance for the overalled workmen about him, their unshaven faces and their surly glances, and promptly went pukka sahib.

"Look at these swine!" he barked into my ear. "That's who we beat our brains out to amuse! Do they appreciate what I've gone through, the aggravation, the sleepless nights I've spent over that show? Give 'em bread and circuses, hey? If I had my way, I'd give 'em something else!"

Heads turned the length of the car, and over the din I detected a subdued muttering like the sans-culottes in a Metro costume film. But Kerr, caught up in a crusading mood in which he identified himself with the Scarlet Pimpernel, was not to be diverted. He launched into a tirade on unions and the New Deal, concluding with a few generalizations that would have abashed even a Republican steering committee. I still marvel that we emerged intact from the Hudson Tubes. Up to the moment we did, I fully expected to expire in a blitzkrieg of lunch-pails.

Thanks to the headwaiter of the Biltmore, a paragon who refused to be intimidated by Kerr's hiccups and our crapulous exteriors, I got some breakfast into my charge, and at eight o'clock, Murray Zweifel appeared. His arrival was the signal for repeated fireworks. We were bracketed with Benedict Arnold and consigned to the devil, roundly notified by Kerr that hell would freeze over before he accompanied us to Boston. We argued and pleaded; at one point, under pretense of visiting the lav, Kerr slipped into a phone booth and was confiding all to Winchell when we extricated him by main force. In the quarter hour before train-time, the fracas degenerated into delirium. Just as the gates were closing, Murray and I bucked our way across Grand Central through a sea of astonished commuters, using Kerr as a battering ram. He was yelling vilification at us, a cataclysmic headache throbbed in my skull, and my reason hung by a thread, but nothing else mattered—the production was saved. From now on, I could relax, for the pathway ahead was strewn with roses. I was fated to learn something about botany, to say nothing of show business.

In the entertainment game, as Sir Arthur Wing Pinero was wont to observe in far loftier language, it don't pay to count your turkeys. At the Hub City premiere of *Sherry Flip*, the traveler curtain failed to open in the conventional fashion. Instead, it billowed out and sank down over the orchestra pit, perceptibly muffling the overture. The musicians fiddled manfully underneath, but Herman Earl's score was too fragile and lilting to overcome the handicap. The comedy, contrariwise, was all too robust —so much so that the police stepped in next day and excised four sketches. The reviews were unanimous. The show, it was agreed, was lavish enough to preclude spending another nickel on it; it should be closed as it stood. And then, on the very threshold of disaster, Kerr decided to rally. He fired the director and restaged the show himself, cut salaries to the bone, and sent a case of cognac to every critic in New York. His acumen bore fruit; we ran five nights there, and those who saw it grow garrulous even today at the memory of *Sherry Flip*. The last time I saw Poultney Kerr, he was a television nabob and beyond mortal ken, but he could not conceal his nostalgia for Broadway. He told me he was mulling an idea for a revue—a smart, intimate romp on the order of *The Garrick Gaieties*.

MONEY TALKS

⤙ ELLERY QUEEN

Blackmail speaks its own peculiar dialect, but it has this advantage over other forms of expression: It is the universal language, understood by all.

Including the Sicilian. Mrs. Alfredo had heard its hissed accents, and she wept.

Ellery thought he had never seen a less likely victim. Mrs. Alfredo was as broad as a *gnocco,* her skin had a time-grated Parmesan look, and her hands had been marinated in the Chianti of hard work. It seemed that she ran a very modest boarding-house in the West Fifties which sagged under a mortgage. How, then, blackmail?

But then he heard about Mrs. Alfredo's daughter Lucia, and Lucia's Tosca, and how encouraging the Metropolitan Opera people had been about Lucia's *"Vissi d'arte, vissi d'amore,"* and Ellery thought he detected the sibilant accent, too.

Lucia's career was in jeopardy.

"On what ground, Mrs. Alfredo?" he asked.

The ground was foreign. In her youth Mrs. Alfredo had been a cook. One summer an employer had taken her to England, in England she had met an Englishman, and the Englishman had married her. Perfidious Albion! Within a month Alfred had vanished with her life's savings. What was worse, although eventually she recovered most of her money, the glamorous Alfred was discovered to possess another wife who claimed, and proved, priority. And what was worse, in inexorable course the poor woman found herself about to have Alfred's baby. Mrs. Alfredo, as she had begun to call herself, fled Bloomsbury for her adopted land, posing as a widow and never telling anyone except Lucia her bigamous secret; and in the prehistoric days when a house could be bought with the widow's mite she had purchased the ancient property in the West Fifties which was now her livelihood and the hope of Lucia's operatic career.

"Long time I scare that Lucia's secret come out," she wept to Ellery, "but then a friend from Bloomsbury write me that Alfred die, so Lucia and I forget our shame. Until now, *signore.* Now it comes out. If I do not pay the money."

The crudely lettered note had been pushed under her bedroom door. Five thousand dollars was demanded for silence about her daughter's illegal state. "How do they know, *Signor* Queen? Never do we tell anyone—never!" The money was to be placed under the loose newel post on the second-floor landing of her house.

"A boarder," said Ellery grimly. "How many boarders do you have, Mrs. Alfredo?"

"Three. Mist' Collins, Mist'—"

"Do you have five thousand dollars, Mrs. Alfredo?"

"Sì. I do not pay off the mortgage—I save for Lucia's Voice Lesson. But if now I pay this money, Maestro Zaggiore give no more lesson! And if I do not pay, it will be known about me, about Lucia. It break Lucia's heart, *signore*. Ruin her career. Already she is cry and cry over this."

"Young hearts take a heap of breaking and careers with real talent behind them don't ruin easily. Take my advice, Mrs. Alfredo: Don't pay."

"No," agreed Mrs. Alfredo with a certain cunning. " 'Cause you catch him quick, hey?"

The next morning Mrs. Alfredo's newest boarder awakened in one of her feather beds to an enchantment. "*Un bel di*," sang Cio-Cio-San, "*vedremo levarsi un fil di fumo. . . .*" The piano sounded as if it had served aboard the U. S. Gunboat *Abraham Lincoln* along with Lieutenant Pinkerton, but the voice coming through the aged walls rang as sweet and rich as a newly minted coin. And Ellery rose, and dressed like a struggling writer just in from Kansas City, and went downstairs to Mrs. Alfredo's dining room determined that Lucia should have her chance.

At breakfast he met Lucia, who was beautiful, and the three boarders, who were not. Mr. Arnold was small, thin, pedantic, and looked like a clerk in a secondhand bookshop, which was exactly what he was; Mr. Bordelaux was medium-sized, fat, garrulous, and looked like a French wine salesman, which was exactly what *he* was; and Mr. Collins was large, powerful, and slangy and if he had not turned out to be a taxicab driver Ellery would have turned in his honorary police badge. They were all three amiable, they took turns ogling Lucia and praising Mrs. Alfredo's *uovo con peperoni*, and they departed—Mr. Arnold for his Cooper Square bookshop, Mr. Bordelaux for his vinous rounds, and Mr. Collins for his battered taxi—in a perfect corona of innocence.

The next three days were incidental. Ellery ransacked Mr. Arnold's room and Mr. Bordelaux's room and Mr. Collins's room. In the evenings and in the mornings he studied his ABCs, as he privately called the three boarders, discussing books with Mr. Arnold, wines with Mr. Bordelaux, and nags and dames with Mr. Collins. He tried to reassure Lucia, who was tragically desperate.

He tried to get Mrs. Alfredo's permission to take the note and her story to the police, for their assistance along certain lines he had in mind; Mrs. Alfredo became hysterical. He advised her to deliver a note to the loose newel post saying that it would take a few days to raise the money. This she consented to do, and Ellery carefully refrained from insomnia that night, merely making sure that entry from outside the building would leave traces. And in the morning the note was gone and there were no traces. . . . Ellery did all the things one does in such cases, and what he gathered for his pains was the knowledge that the blackmailer was Mr. Arnold the book clerk, or Mr. Bordelaux the wine drummer, or Mr. Collins the taxi driver, and he had known that from the beginning.

But the fourth morning dawned with a bang. The emotional hand of Mrs. Alfredo was on his bedroom door, and its owner cried doom.

"My Lucia! She lock herself in her room! She does not answer! She is at least dead!"

Ellery soothed the frantic woman and hurried into the hall. From three doorways three heads protruded.

"Something wrong?" exclaimed Mr. Arnold.

"Is it that there is a fire?" cried Mr. Bordeaux.

"What gives?" growled Mr. Collins.

Ellery tried Lucia's door. It was latched from inside. He knocked. No answer. He listened. He heard nothing.

"Dr. Santelli!" moaned Mrs. Alfredo. "I get *il dottore!*"

"Do that," said Ellery. "Collins, help me break this door in."

"Lemme at it," said the powerful Mr. Collins.

But the old door was like iron.

"The ax of the fire," howled Mr. Bordelaux; and he flew down the stairs after Mrs. Alfredo, carpet slippers flapping.

"Here," panted Mr. Arnold, appearing with a chair. "Let's have a look through that fanlight." He scrambled onto the chair and peered through the transom above the door. "She's on the bed. She's been sick— She's just lying there—"

"Any blood, Arnold?" asked Ellery anxiously.

"No. . . . But there's a box of sweets. And a tin of something—"

"Oh, no," groaned Ellery. "Can you make out the label?"

Mr. Arnold's Adam's crabapple bobbed before the little rectangular window above the door. "It looks like . . . rat poison."

At which Mr. Bordelaux appeared with the fire ax and Mrs. Alfredo with an excited gentleman in his undershirt who looked like Arturo Toscanini. They all tumbled in to find that Lucia had attempted to commit suicide by filling some chocolates with rat poison and bravely swallowing them.

"*Molto, molto,*" said Dr. Santelli. "Her tummy rejects. All to go out!" And later, the doctor called Mrs. Alfredo and Ellery in, and he said, "Lucia. *Cara.* Open the eye."

"Mama," quavered Lucia.

"*'Bina,*" wept Mama.

But Ellery set Mama firmly to one side. "Lucia, the Met needs you—believe me! You're never to do such a foolish thing again. Anyway, you won't have to, because now I know which one of Mama's boarders has been trying to blackmail her, and I think I can assure you that he won't try it again."

And later Ellery said to the silent man holding the suitcase, "My clients will press no charge so long as you're smart enough to keep their secret. I might add, before you go, that you're far too careless to make a successful blackmailer."

"Careless?" said the man with the suitcase, sullenly.

"Oh, criminally. Mrs. Alfredo and Lucia never have told anyone about the illegal union. So the blackmailer must have learned about it from the bigamist himself. But since Alfred was an Englishman who lived—and died—in England, the great likelihood was that the blackmailer was English, too, you see.

"You tried hard to conceal it, but in the excitement of this morning's events you slipped. Only an Englishman would have called a rectangular transom a 'fanlight,' chocolates 'sweets,' and a can of poison a 'tin.' So if you're ever tempted to stray from your bookselling to try a scoundrelly stunt like this again—watch your language, Mr. Arnold!"

A FUNNY THING HAPPENED ON THE WAY TO THE THEATRE

⌇⌇ BILLY ROSE

I was born the night President McKinley was shot, and a lot of fellows around Broadway will tell you they shot the wrong man.

The coming-out party took place on a kitchen table in a tenement on the lower East Side. When my mother first saw me, she prophesied, "Some day he'll be President." My father looked at me and said, "He's all right, I guess, but what we really needed was an icebox."

My Pop was what you might call a non-persuasive salesman. When fringe was the fashion, his sample-case would only contain passementerie. When people were crying for passementerie, he would only handle fringe. Consequently, money was a sometime thing around our house, and for years we changed residence every few months. It was cheaper to move than pay rent.

When I went to the High School of Commerce in 1915, the family stock was still empty. It was imperative that I learn something I could merchandise quickly, and so I concentrated on shorthand and typewriting. By working like an Igorot, I got to be something of a shorthand expert, and in 1917 I left school, went to Washington and got myself a job as stenographer with the War Industries Board. There I met its chairman, Bernard M. Baruch. He took a shine to me.

I was several hundred dollars ahead when the war ended and for reasons I can't remember, I decided to take a trip around the world. But my money lasted only as far as New Orleans. On the way back to New York, the boat I was on rammed and sank a freighter in a fog off Cape Hatteras. One of the survivors we picked up was a pretty girl named Edna Harris. When I handed her one of the five life-preservers I was wearing, it started a beautiful friendship. Before we docked, I made a date to see her in New York.

The first night I took her out, we walked up Broadway. Though I was crowding twenty at the time, I had never been on the Big Street at night. But Edna knew her way around. She steered me to Wolpin's, one of those underground delicatessens where celebrities gathered to eat the life-giving pastrami and quaff great beakers of celery tonic.

"That's Fred Fischer," she said, pointing to a man with an outsized head. "He wrote 'Dardanella.' And that's Walter Donaldson, the writer of 'Mammy.'"

"What kind of money do they make?" I asked.

"No telling," said Edna. "Couple of thousand a week, maybe."

"How long has this been going on?" I said to myself.

From then on, I did most of my eating at Wolpin's, and after a while got to know most of the songwriters. In those days I was a simple-hearted little bloke. My ambitions were to make a million dollars and marry Mary Pickford. I believed what everybody believed in 1922—that U. S. Steel would hit 500, that nice girls didn't kiss the first time you took them out, and that Heaven was not for Democrats.

One night at Wolpin's I asked Harry Ruby, the composer, "Has anybody ever thought of rhyming 'June' with 'macaroon'?"

The entire delicatessen applauded and Harry shook my hand. A waiter handed me a pencil and a clean menu and said, "Mr. Rose, you're in business."

Six cups of coffee later, I dotted the last "i" on my first masterpiece.

> *Does the Spearmint lose its flavor on the bedpost overnight?*
> *If you paste it on the left side will you find it on the right?*
> *When you chew it in the morning will it be too hard to bite?*
> *Does the Spearmint lose its flavor on the bedpost overnight?*

It was published by Watterson, Berlin and Snyder, and the early ten-watt radio transmitters smallpoxed the air with it. I got an appointment with a Wrigley executive and told him I thought I was entitled to some money for my efforts on behalf of his product. He booted me out of his office without so much as a pack of gum for my trouble.

But I got my revenge. The time bomb I lit in 1922 exploded in 1939 with the Pepsi-Cola jingle. The rest, God help us, is history. *I wrote the first singing commercial.*

There, I've said it! And I'm glad. For years I've been walking around with this secret, fraternizing with people who are kind to small animals and bathe every day. Now I've come clean.

Chop me up in little pieces and feed me to the lions. You won't hear a peep out of me.

Besides the Spearmint classic, I was responsible for "You Tell Her, I Stutter," and "You Gotta See Mama Every Night." These songs made quite a bit of money, and the following year I invested some of this loot in the nightclub business—principally, I think, because I wanted to wear a black hat and meet some girls. My first waterhole was hidden over a garage on 56th Street near Sixth Avenue. The iron-stomached citizens who survived the Noble Experiment may remember it as the Backstage Club—the place where Helen Morgan first climbed up on a piano to avoid the tables which were advancing upon her across the dance floor.

The Backstage Club represented an outlay of $4,000. It amortized itself the opening night.

A few months later I opened a second trap on Fifth Avenue—I wanted to meet a better class of girls. It was called the Fifth Avenue Club, and it exhaled so much fake swank that on opening night my French headwaiter suggested I stay out of sight in the office. The show was written by a couple of kids fresh out of Columbia—Rodgers and Hart. I had really arrived socially. My new neighbors included Samuel Untermyer, the Union League Club, and John D. Rockefeller, Sr.

Eyebrows shot up all over the neighborhood the night we opened. John D. was at the age when he needed his sleep something fierce, and when my bug-eyed musicians erupted with "Somebody Stole My Gal" at four in the morning he hollered copper at the top of his ancient lungs. A dozen of New York's Finest roared up on motorcycles, but when they found I wasn't selling whiskey, they compromised on making me mute half my trumpets.

To keep the club exclusive, I slapped on a $5 cover charge. Well, that did it. Pretty soon it was so exclusive the waiters were playing penny casino with each other. In a couple of months I was feeling through the pockets of old suits for lunch money.

One night I got an idea. I would sell my club to a blonde who was running a speakeasy in Greenwich Village. Her boy friend was one of our leading bathtub chemists.

I went down to the Village to see her. "Queenie," I said, "this speak is no showcase for a woman of your talents. You belong on Fifth Avenue."

"You can say that again, dearie," said Queenie, "but what would I do up there? I can't sing and my gentleman friend made me give up hoofin'."

"All great women of the world have had salons," I said airily. "Du Barry, Pompadour, Marie Antoinette. Princes and statesmen flocked around just to hear these women talk."

I moved in for the kill. "Get your boy friend to buy my club for you. Advertise yourself as 'Mistress of Conversation.' Wear a stylish gown—something transparent and expensive. And when the customers arrive, talk to them—just talk to them. It'll be tremendous!"

Queenie bought the dream, and next morning the bathtub chemist bought my sick little nightclub. He ran big ads, billing her as "Mistress of Conversation." But the place folded in a few weeks.

Poor Queenie! Though she was willing to talk to anybody, nobody wanted to talk to *her*.

After the Fifth Avenue Club, I went back to songwriting. You may remember one of the ditties I wrote around that time—"Barney Google with the Goo-Goo-Googly Eyes." Deems Taylor said it was probably the worst song in the history of the music business —but Deems always was a jealous fellow.

In 1926 I wrote a vaudeville act for Fanny Brice. During its out-of-town tryouts, I found that Fanny and I liked the same jokes and disliked the same people. In 1928 I persuaded the great comedienne to become Mrs. Rose. The day she did, I automatically became known as Mr. Brice. You see, in those days, Fanny's house was a hangout for the Whitneys and Wanamakers, and outside of Irving Berlin, a pop songwriter was considered small spuds.

One night C. B. Dillingham attended one of Fanny's at-homes. I noticed that everybody made a fuss over the producer. A few nights later a similar fuss was made over Ziegfeld. "If you want your name back," I said to myself, "you'll have to become a producer."

And so, in 1931 I made my bow on Broadway with a musical revue called *Sweet and Low*. Though I had worked on it for a year and put every penny I had in it, it wasn't much of a show. An angry critic dismissed it with the line, "The Rose that does not smell so sweet."

The day after it closed a press agent named Ned Alvord came into my office. He was sporting a seersucker cutaway, a derby hat and a turned-around collar like a minister. In a train-whistle voice he announced I could get my dough back if I had the guts to juice up the show, take it to the hinterlands, and sell it like Barnum used to sell his circus. He gave off sparks and I caught fire.

I went out and hocked my ASCAP royalties, revamped *Sweet and Low,* and changed the title to *Crazy Quilt.* And I'll never forget how Ned advertised this pale little revue—"A Saturnalia of Wanton Rhythm"—"Voluptuous Houris"—"Dashing Demoiselles" —every sentence ending with "Since the Dawn of Time!"

When I pointed out that we were carrying only a few curtains and eighteen bandy-legged chorus girls, Ned fog-horned, "Take the money and run for the train." And for a screamingly successful year that's just what we did!

It was Ned who taught me that the short cut to the customer's poke is by way of the roadside fence—that "bill it like a circus" sells more tickets than "to be or not to be."

My first lesson in paper-and-paste came when I commissioned a lad with a lavender tie to design a twenty-four-sheet for our traveling show. He delivered a layout in delicate blues and pinks. I showed it to Alvord. "It stinks, sir," he said.

"But it's pretty," I protested.

"Then hang it in your bedroom," he snapped. "It's a foggy night in Kansas and our poster is on an outhouse. I want to see it, sir."

We settled on something in black and yellow—you couldn't

look at it without smoked glasses. And the only switch I've made in twenty years was when I ordered the posters for *Carmen Jones*. Instead of yellow and black, I changed the color scheme to black and yellow.

Shortly after *Crazy Quilt* closed, I produced a play called *The Great Magoo* by Ben Hecht and Gene Fowler. It lasted a week. The following year, I opened a theatre restaurant called the Casino de Paree. It was bankrolled by a group of gentlemen whose pictures have appeared in some of our finest post offices.

A few months later, I ripped the insides out of Arthur Hammerstein's pretty theatre on 53rd and Broadway and opened another cabaret called the The Billy Rose Music Hall. Its feature number was a potpouri of oldtime vaudevillians—fire-eaters, acrobats and Swiss bell-ringers—who did an abbreviated version of their turns. This was my first meeting with the pretty lady called "Nostalgia" and we've been buddies ever since.

The electric sign on this music hall was a seven-day wonder on Broadway. It was eighteen stories high and the mazdas spelled out just two words—"BILLY ROSE." The first night it was burning, I went outside to admire it. As I stood on the corner, I heard someone ask, "Billy Rose? Who dat?"

"That's Fanny Brice's husband," someone answered. I finally took care of this Mr. Brice situation a few months later when I gave birth to a theatrical dream child called *Jumbo*. No year in my life has been wackier than the one devoted to producing this musical circus at the New York Hippodrome. The author, director, and player credits read like a Burke's Peerage of the theatre— Hecht and MacArthur, Rodgers and Hart, John Murray Anderson, George Abbott, Jimmy Durante, Paul Whiteman and his orchestra.

This country-sized candy box was largely financed by Jock Whitney and his sister, Joan, a couple of amiable tots whose Pop had left them $175,000,000. As production costs mounted, the standard gag around Broadway was, "This will make Rose or break Whitney."

Carried away by the notion of marrying a circus to a musical comedy, we showed no more respect for the law of gravity than do the characters in a Silly Symphony. The opening number was climaxed by shooting an adagio dancer out of a cannon into the arms of her partner fifty feet away. Dohoes, an educated white horse from Copenhagen, did everything but play first base. In one sequence a troupe of daredevils indulged in fingertip balancing over an open cage of lions.

But *Jumbo* was too big for its cash registers. Though it received superb notices and played to over a million customers, it lost money. A few years ago the Whitneys got some of it back when Metro bought the movie rights. I don't know when the studio is going to get around to making this picture, but before it does, I would suggest that it send the director to New York and instruct him to stand still some night near the parking space at 43rd Street and Sixth Avenue where the old Hippodrome stood. If he listens closely, he'll still hear them yocking it up at what drama critics agree was the biggest laugh in the history of show business. It came near the end of the first act when a sheriff caught Jimmy Durante trying to steal an elephant.

"Where are ya going with that elephant?" yelled the copper.

"What elephant?" asked Jimmy.

Finding the elephant for the title role in *Jumbo* was quite a chore. A fellow who had sold me some monkeys said I might be able to rent one from Mr. Charles W. Beall in Oceanside, Long Island.

According to the monkey man, this Mr. Beall was quite a fellow. From Monday to Friday, he was vice-president of the Chase National Bank; Saturdays and Sundays he devoted to training wild animals.

The following Saturday I drove out to Oceanside. The monkey man hadn't overstated the case. On his beautiful ten-acre estate, Mr. Beall, a fine figure of a tycoon, maintained one of the most complete private zoos in America. In addition to lions, tigers, leopards, and black panthers, his cages contained at least one each of the animals on exhibit at the Bronx Zoo.

At the house, a butler told me Mr. Beall was working out with the animals in a cage back of the garage. I walked around and watched the amateur Clyde Beatty. He handled the whip and chair like a pro, and the big cats were slinking around as though they had guilt complexes.

"What can I do for you, young man?" he said when the beasts were all up on their inverted tubs.

"Want to sell, lease or rent an elephant?" I called through the bars.

Mr. Beall clicked the cage door open. "Come in," he said. "They won't hurt you."

You can judge how badly I needed an elephant when I tell you I walked into that cage.

"Afraid I can't do anything for you," said the banker after I had explained my problem. "I'm down to six elephants, and I like to have at least that many around. They relax me."

After lunch he showed me around his place. I didn't see any women on the estate and I got the impression he was a bachelor.

On the way back to town, I got to wondering about his private life. What sort of women, for instance, would appeal to a millionaire who hobnobbed with lions and panthers?

A few years later, the tabloids told me. It appeared that Mr. Beall had hired a vaudeville performer named Nana Bates as secretary. He had seen this lady do a tiger dance in a local theatre and had been impressed by her qualifications.

According to the tabloids, Mr. Beall had gotten along fine with his secretary until he sent her to Hollywood on business. During her absence, he had made the mistake of hiring another actress-stenographer. When the Tiger Woman returned unexpectedly and found her pretty successor on the porch, she reached for a hatpin.

The two shorthand experts indulged in some fancy scratching and floor-rolling. A neighbor phoned the Oceanside police. The old financier was caught in the middle—something which hadn't happened to him either on Wall Street or in the lions' cage.

Most of the later rounds were staged in court, where the judge finally told the banker to make up his mind which secretary he wanted. Mr. Beall chose the Tiger Woman.

While these legal shenanigans were going on, I happened to be driving through Oceanside. I found Mr. Beall sitting on a stool in the lions' cage. The big cats were on their tubs, unusually quiet. The amateur trainer's face was all scratched up and there were bits of court plaster on his neck and hands.

"Did a cat take a poke at you?" I asked.

The financier nodded. "Yes," he said. "One of the two-legged ones."

"What's the idea of sitting out here?" I said.

Mr. Beall got up, walked over to one of the lions and scratched it behind the ears. "Frankly," he sighed, "this is the only place on the estate where I feel perfectly safe."

On the strength of the *Jumbo* press notices, Amon Carter and the other city farmers of Forth Worth asked me to stage the Texas Centennial Exposition of 1936-37. Dallas, thirty-two miles away, was preparing a $25,000,000 industrial fair, and "Little Old Cowtown" wanted a show that would steal the spotlight from its rival.

Carter told me the job had to be done in a hundred days and asked what I wanted for my services. Taking a deep breath, I said, "A hundred thousand dollars." The city fathers conferred for all of three minutes and agreed. And if I may be pardoned a brag, I think I earned my fee the next day when I coined the slogan, "Dallas for Education, Fort Worth for Entertainment."

I arrived in Forth Worth with a small boy's notions of the Wild West. As a kid, I had read Zane Grey with a flashlight under the blankets after my old man had chased me off to bed. In the nickelodeons I had whooped "Look out" when the bad guy snuck up behind William S. Hart.

Naturally, when I planned the shows for the Exposition, I included one with cowboys and Indians. I labeled it "The Last Frontier," and you'll get some idea of the dimensions of this hootnanny when I tell you we used a quarter of a million dollars' worth of livestock in it.

I started out by hiring the cowboy stars who had won important prize money at every rodeo from Pendleton to Madison Square Garden. These lads were wonderful at riding, roping, and bulldogging the wild steer. But they were not so good when it came to Deadeye Dick stuff with a pistol.

The cowboys could draw quick and shoot straight, provided the target was man-sized and close-up. But when I wanted somebody to pop a clay pipe out of a girl's mouth at fifty feet, I had to import the national pistol champion, a slicker from Brooklyn who had studied marksmanship in a Coney Island shooting gallery. The cowboys oohed and aahed when they saw this kind of shooting, and my kid dreams got their first kick in the chaps.

But that was nothing compared with what the Indians did to my illusions. One day I called Carter and told him I needed some redskins for a big war-dance number. "How many?" he said, as if I had asked for desk blotters.

"Oh, a hundred and fifty," I said.

A couple of weeks later, a gent walked into the air-conditioned blockhouse in which I was officing. "I got your Indians," he said. "Where shall I put them?" I went outside and looked. There they were, blankets, feathers, papooses and goats. It looked like an explosion in a paint factory.

"They're all yours," said the agent. "Sign here."

"Have your people down at the Last Frontier arena at five this afternoon," I told the boss Indian. "I want to see them dance."

When I got to the arena a couple of braves were half-heartedly knuckling tomtoms. The Indians had already been dancing for half an hour, but their movements had as much abandon as those of a man standing in a moving bus.

"Tell 'em to cut loose," I said to the agent.

"They've cut," he replied. "Takes 'em a little time to warm up. They ought to git goin' good along about midnight. By tomorrow afternoon they should be jumpin'."

The Last Frontier opened with a parade of covered wagons instead of a war dance. . . .

I would have written off the whole Wild West legend as Gene Autry publicity except for one incident. One night there was a riot on the Midway. Somebody claimed he'd been cheated and the first thing I knew a hundred people were swinging at each other.

I phoned for the Rangers. A few minutes later one of them showed up. He walked into where they were fighting. Word spread like wild-fire through the melee that a Ranger was there, and the brawl was over in a minute.

As I watched him walk away, it was with the same eyes that used to read Zane Grey under the blanket.

One number in The Last Frontier was built around a song

called "Memories of Buffalo Bill." I thought it would be a nice touch to close this scene with a herd of buffalo coming down the hills and exiting stage right to eight bars of music.

I phoned Carter. "Three dozen buffalo?" said Amon. "Will do!"

My good right arm in staging the Exposition was John Murray Anderson, the soft-spoken Englishman who has fashioned a score of musical successes on Broadway and Piccadilly. The night before the Exposition opened, I was scooting around on a motorcycle, putting Big Genius touches to this and that.

I dragged Murray away from the platoons of girls he was directing at the Casa Manana cabaret and took him in my sidecar to the dress rehearsal of The Last Frontier. Anderson had no zest for this Wild West show, but he went to work setting the light-cues in his best Nelson Monument manner.

Around four in the morning, we got to the Buffalo Bill sequence. I went over the number with Murray. It started with half a dozen cowboys around a campfire on one of the prop hills. To the plunking of a guitar, one of them would sing about his memories of Cody's famous Wild West show. As he finished the first chorus, the thirty-six buffalo would enter and come down the hills while the orchestra went heavy on the fiddles. Behind the smelly monsters would come a man on horseback, togged out like the Buffalo Bill of the posters.

I told Murray I wanted a soulful shade of blue to light my herd of buffalo. There are many blues a director can choose from, ranging from the sky-blue of gelatin No. 29 to the purplish-blue of gelatin No. 37. At his seat in the grandstand, Anderson picked up a portable phone and called the stage-manager behind the hills two blocks away. "Turn on the 29 blues," he said.

A moment later the giant sun-arcs flooded the field. Then Murray said in a bored voice, "Now the buffalo, please."

Zowie! They stormed out of the chutes and charged down the hills hellbent for the Gulf of Mexico. When they were halfway down my man-made cliffs, Murray raised a well-manicured hand as if he were addressing a line of Shubert chorus boys.

"Hold it please," he said. "Change that gelatin to a 31."

The hit of the Exposition was the Casa Manana cabaret, featuring Sally Rand. Her fan-is-quicker-than-the-eye routine went over big with the art-conscious customers that summer.

One night, Governor Dave Sholtz of Florida was in the house. I stopped by his table to ask if he'd mind being introduced from the stage before the show. Sholtz said he'd be honored.

As I started to walk away he asked if Miss Sally Rand were around. Said he had met her some years back when she played the Citrus Circuit in his state. I told him Sally was in her dressing room and offered to take him backstage.

When the Governor and I entered Sally's room, she was flat on the floor, wrapped in something pink, her chin propped up on her hands. And she was reading the Bible!

Scoffers will please leave quietly. Sally is always reading something or other. That summer it was the Bible straight through from Genesis to Revelation.

After Sally and the Governor had swapped hellos, he picked up the Good Book and said, "Let me read you a short passage which has always been a source of comfort to me." He turned to the Book of Psalms and began reading quietly.

It was almost show time. I heard Whiteman's orchestra tuning up and slipped out of the dressing room. A few minutes later I was at the center microphone on the big stage. As I introduced the first couple of celebrities, I kept looking off-stage towards Sally's room.

Someone in Sholtz's party hollered, "Introduce the Governor of Florida!"

"I'm sorry," I lied. "The Governor's talking long-distance to Tallahassee."

I wasn't going to stand there with my bare face hanging out and tell four thousand people that the Governor of Florida couldn't appear because he was reading the Bible in Sally Rand's dressing room!

THE ETIQUETTE OF ENGAGEMENT S AND WEDDINGS

⟨ꝰ DONALD OGDEN STEWART

The historic aspect

"Matrimony," sings Homer, the poet, "is a holy estate and not lightly to be entered into." The "old Roman" is right. A modern wedding is one of the most intricate and exhausting of social customs. Young men and women of our better classes are now forced to devote a large part of their lives to acting as brides, grooms, ushers and bridesmaids at various elaborate nuptials. Weeks are generally required in preparation for an up-to-date wedding; months are necessary in recovering from such an affair. Indeed, some of the participants, notably the bride and groom, never quite get over the effects of a marriage.

It was not "always thus." Time was when the wedding was a comparatively simple affair. In the Paleolithic Age, for example (as Mr. H. G. Wells of England points out in his able *Outline of History*), there is no evidence of any particular ceremony conjunctive with the marriage of "a male and a female." Even with the advent of Neolithic man, a wedding seems to have been consummated by the rather simple process of having the bridegroom crack the bride over the head with a plain, unornamented stone ax. There were no ushers—no bridesmaids. But shortly after that (c. 10,329-30 B.C. to be exact) two young Neoliths named Haig, living in what is now supposed to be Scotland, discovered that the prolonged distillation of common barley resulted in the creation of an amber-colored liquid which, when taken internally, produced a curious and not unpleasant effect.

This discovery had—and still has—a remarkable effect upon the celebration of the marriage rite. Gradually there grew up around the wedding a number of customs. With the Haig brothers' discovery of Scotch whiskey began, as a matter of course, the institution of the "bachelor dinner." "Necessity is the mother of invention," and exactly twelve years after the first "bachelor dinner" came the discovery of bicarbonate of soda. From that time down to the present day the history of the etiquette of weddings has been that of an increasing number of intricate forms and ceremonies, each age having added its particular bit of ritual. The modern wedding may be said to be, therefore, almost an *Outline of History* itself.

Announcing the engagement

Let us begin, first of all, with the duties of one of the minor characters at a wedding—the Groom. Suppose that you are an eligible young man named Richard Roe, who has just become "engaged" to a young lady named Dorothy Doe. If you really intend to "marry the girl," it is customary that some formal announcement of the engagement be made, for which you must have the permission of Miss Dorothy and her father. It is not generally difficult to become engaged to most girls, but it will surprise you to discover how hard it is to get the young lady whom you believe to be your fiancée to consent to a public announcement of the fact. The reason for this probably is that an engagement which has been "announced" often leads to matrimony, and matrimony, in polite society, often lasts for several years.

After you have secured the girl's permission, it is next necessary that you notify her father of the engagement. In this particular case, as he happens to be your employer, the notification can take place in his office. First of all, however, it would be advisable to prepare some sort of speech in advance. Aim to put him as far as possible at his ease, lead up to the subject gradually and tactfully. Abruptness is never "good form." The following is suggested as a possible model.

"Good morning, Mr. Doe, say, I heard a good story from a traveling salesman last night. It seems that there was a young married couple—(here insert a good story about a young married couple). Wasn't that *rich?* Yes, sir, marriage is a great thing—a great institution. Every young man ought to get married, don't you think?

You do? Well, Mr. Doe, I've got a surprise for you (here move toward the door). I'm going to (here open the door) marry (step out of the room) your daughter" (close the door quickly).

The bride-to-be

Before the public announcement of the engagement it is customary for the bride-to-be to write personal letters to all other young men to whom she happens to be engaged at the time. These notes should be kindly, sympathetic and tactful. The same note can be written to all, provided there is no chance of their comparing notes. The following is suggested:

"Dear Bob—

Bob, I want you to be the very first to know that I am engaged to Richard Roe. I want you to like him, Bob, because he is a fine fellow and I would rather have you like him than anyone I know. I feel that he and I shall be very happy together, and I want you to be the first to know about it. Your friendship will always remain one of the brightest things in my life, Bob, but, of course, I probably won't be able to go to the Aiken dance with you now. Please don't tell anybody about it yet. I shall never forget the happy times you and I had together, Bob, and will you please return those silly letters of mine. I am sending you yours."

The engagement luncheon

The engagement is generally announced at a luncheon given by the parents of the prospective bride. This is usually a small affair, only fifteen or twenty of the most intimate friends of the engaged "couple" being invited. It is one of the customs of engagement luncheons that all the guests shall be tremendously surprised at the news, and great care should be taken to aid them in carrying out this tradition. On the invitations, for example, should be written some misleading phrase, such as "To meet General Pershing" or "Not to Announce the Engagement of our Daughter."

The announcement itself, which should be made soon after the guests are seated, offers a splendid opportunity for the display of originality and should aim to afford the guest a surprise and perhaps a laugh, for laughter of a certain quiet kind is often welcome at social functions. One of the most favored methods of announcing an engagement is by the use of symbolic figures embodying the names of the affianced pair. Thus, for example, in the case of the present engagement of Richard Roe to Dorothy Doe it would be "unique" to have the first course at luncheon consist of a diminutive candy or papier-maché doe seated amorously upon a heart-shaped order of shad roe. The guests will at first be mystified, but soon cries of "Oh, how sweet!" will arise and congratulations are then in order. Great care should be taken, however, that the symbolic figures are not misunderstood; it would be extremely embarrassing, for example, if in the above instance, a young man named "Shad" or "Aquarium" were to receive the congratulations instead of the proper person.

Other suggestions for symbolistic announcements of some of the more common names are as follows:

"Cohan–O'Brien"—ice cream cones on a plate of O'Brien potatoes.

"Ames–Green"—green ice cream in the shape of a man aiming at something.

"Thorne–Hoyt"—figure of a man from Brooklyn pulling a thorn from foot with expression on his face signifying "This hoits."

"Bullitt–Bartlett"—Bartlett pears full of small .22 or .33 calibre bullets.

"Tweed–Ellis"—frosted cake in the shape of Ellis Island with a solitary figure of a man in a nice fitting tweed suit.

"Gordon–Fuller"—two papier-maché figures—one representing a young man full of Gordon gin, the other representing a young man fuller.

"Hatch–Gillette"—figure of a chicken surprised at having hatched a safety razor.

"Graves–Colgate"—figure of a man brushing his teeth in a cemetery.

"Heinz–Fish"—57 assorted small fish tastily arranged on one plate.

Selecting the bridal party

As soon as the engagement has been announced it is the duty of the prospective bride to select a maid-of-honor and eight or ten bridesmaids, while the groom must choose his best man and ushers. In making these selections it should be carefully borne in mind that no wedding party is complete without the following:

2 bridesmaids who never danced more than once with anybody.
1 bridesmaid who danced twice with the Prince of Wales.
1 bridesmaid who doesn't "pet."
1 bridesmaid who was expelled from Miss Spence's.
1 bridesmaid who talks "Southern."
1 bridesmaid who rowed on the crew at Wellesley.
1 usher who doesn't drink anything.
9 ushers who drink anything.

In some localities, following the announcement, it is customary for the bride's friends to give for her a number of "showers." These are for the purpose of providing her with various necessities for her wedded household life. These affairs should be informal and only her dearest or wealthiest friends should be invited. A clever bride will generally arrange secretly for several of these "showers" by promising a certain percentage (usually 15% of the gross up to $500.00 and 25% bonus on all over that amount) to the friend who gives the party. Some of the more customary "showers" of common household articles for the new bride are toothpaste, milk of magnesia, screen doors, copies of Service's poems, Cape Cod lighters, pictures of "Age of Innocence" and back numbers of the *Atlantic Monthly*.

Invitations and wedding presents

The proper time to send out invitations to a wedding is between two and three weeks before the day set for the ceremony, although the out-of-town invitations should be mailed in plenty of time to allow the recipient to purchase and forward a suitable present. As the gifts are received, a check mark should be placed after the name of the donor, together with a short description of the present and an estimate as to its probable cost. This list is to be used later, at the wedding reception, in determining the manner in which the bride is to greet the various guests. It has been found helpful by many brides to devise some sort of memory system whereby certain names immediately suggest certain responses, thus,

"Mr. Snodgrass—copy of *Highways and Byways in Old France*—c. $6.50—"how do you do, Mr. Snodgrass, have you met my mother?"

"Mr. Brackett—Solid silver candlesticks—$68.50"—"hello, Bob, you old peach. How about a kiss?"

The real festivities of a wedding start about three days before the ceremony, with the arrival of the "wedding party," in which party the most responsible position is that of best man. Let us suppose that you are to be the best man at the Roe-Doe nuptials. What are your duties?

In the first place, you must prepare yourself for the wedding by a course of training extending for over a month or more prior to the actual event. It should be your aim to work yourself into such a condition that you can go for three nights without sleep, talk for hours to the most impossibly stupid of young women, and consume an unending amount of alcohol. You are then prepared for the bachelor dinner, the bridal dinner, the bridesmaids, the wedding, and the wedding reception.

Duties of the best man

Upon your arrival in the city where the wedding is to take place you will be met by the bridegroom, who will take you to the home of the bride where you are to stay. There you are met by the bride's father. "This is my best man," says the groom. "The best man?" replies her father. "Well, may the best man win." At once you reply, "Ha! Ha! Ha!" He then says, "Is this your first visit to Chicago?" to which the correct answer is, "Yes, sir, but I hope it isn't my last."

The bride's mother then appears. "This is my best man," says the groom. "Well," says she, "remember—the best man doesn't always win." "Ha! Ha! Ha!" you at once reply. "Is this your first visit to Chicago?" says she, to which you answer, "Yes—but I hope it isn't my last."

You are then conducted to your room, where you are left alone to unpack. In a few minutes the door will open and a small boy enter. This is the brother of the bride. You smile at him pleasantly and remark, "Is this your first visit to Chicago?" "What are you doing?" is his answer. "Unpacking," you reply. "What's that?" says he. "A cutaway," you reply. "What's that?" says he. "A collar bag." "What's that?" "A dress shirt." "What's that?" says he. "Another dress shirt." "What's that?" says he. "Say, listen," you reply, "don't I hear some one calling you?" "No," says he, "what's that?" "That," you reply, with a sigh of relief, "is a razor. Here—take it and play with it." In three minutes, if you have any luck at all, the bride's brother will have cut himself severely in several places which will cause him to run crying from the room. You can then finish unpacking.

The bride's tea

The first function of the pre-nuptial festivities is generally a tea at the bride's home, where the ushers and bridesmaids meet to become "acquainted." It is your duty, as best man, to go to the hotel where the ushers are stopping and bring them to this tea. Just as you will leave on this mission the groom will whisper in your ear, "For God's sake, remember to tell them that her father and mother are terribly opposed to drinking in any form." This is an awfully good joke on her father and mother.

As you step out of the hotel elevator you hear at the end of the hall a chorus shouting, "Mademoiselle from Armentieres—*parlez vous!*" Those are your ushers.

Opening the door of the room you step forward and announce, "Fellows, we have got to go to a tea right away. Come on—let's go." At this, ten young men in cutaways will stand up and shout, "Yeaaa—the best man—give the best man a drink!" From then on, at twelve minute intervals, it is your duty to say, "Fellows, we have got to go to a tea right away. Come on—let's go." Each time you will be handed another drink, which you may take with either your right or left hand.

After an hour the telephone will ring. It will be the groom. He will say, "Everybody is waiting for you and the ushers," to which you reply, "We are just leaving." He then says, "And don't forget to tell them what I told you about her father and mother."

You then hang up the receiver, take a drink in one hand and say, "Fellows, I have a very solemn message for you. It's a message which is of deep importance to each one of us. Fellows—her father and mother object to the use of alcohol in any form."

This statement will be greeted with applause and cheers. You will all then take one more drink, put on your silk hats and gray gloves, and leave the room singing, "Her father and mother object to drink—*parlez vous.*"

The tea given by the bride's parents is generally a small affair to which only the members of the wedding party are invited. When you and the ushers arrive, you will find the bride, the maid of honor and the bridesmaids waiting for you. As you enter the room, make a polite bow to the bride's father and mother, and be sure to apologize for your lateness. Nothing so betrays the social "oil can" as a failure to make a plausible excuse for tardiness. Whenever you are late for a party you must always have ready some good reason for your fault, such as, "Excuse me, Mrs. Doe, I'm afraid I am a little late, but you see, just as I was dressing, this filling dropped out of my tooth and I had to have it put back in." If the host and hostess seem to doubt your statement, it would be well to show them the recalcitrant filling in question, although if they are "well-bred" they will probably in most cases take you at your word.

The maid of honor

You and the ushers will then be introduced to the bridesmaids and the maid of honor. As you meet this latter young lady, who is the bride's older sister and, of course, your partner for the remainder of the wedding festivities, she will say, "The best man? Well, they say the best man wins . . . Ha! Ha! Ha!" This puts her in G6 without further examination, and your only hope of prolonging your life throughout the next two days lies in the frequent and periodic administration of stimulants.

The bachelor dinner and after

That evening the groom gives for the best man and the ushers what is known as a "bachelor dinner." It is his farewell to his men friends as he passes out of the state of bachelorhood. The formal passing out generally occurs toward the end of the dinner, and is a quaint ceremony participated in by most of those present.

It is customary for the best man to wake up about noon of the following day. You will not have the slightest idea as to where you are or how you got there. You will be wearing your dress trousers, your stiff or pleated bosom dress shirt, black socks and pumps, and the coat of your pajamas. In one hand you will be clutching a chrysanthemum. After a few minutes there will come a low moan from the next bed. That is usually the groom, also in evening dress with the exception that he has tried to put on the trousers of your pajamas over his dress trousers. You then say, "What happened?" to which he replies, "Oh, Judas." You wait several minutes. In the next room you hear the sound of a shower bath and some one whistling. The bath stops; the whistling continues. The door then opens and there enters one of the ushers. He is the usher who always "feels great" the next day after the bachelor dinner. He says to you, "Well, boys, you look all in." You do not reply. He continues, "Gosh, I feel fine." You make no response. He then begins to chuckle, "I don't suppose you remember," he says, "what you said to the bride's mother when I brought you home last night." You sit quickly up in bed. "What did I say?" you ask. "Was I tight?" "Were you tight?" he replies, still chuckling. "Don't you remember what you said? And don't you remember trying to get the bride's father to slide down the banisters with you? Were you tight— Oh, my gosh!" He then exits, chuckling. Statistics of several important life insurance companies show that that type of man generally dies a violent death before the age of thirty.

The rehearsal

The rehearsal for the wedding is usually held in the church on the afternoon preceding the day of the nuptials. The ushers, of course, are an hour late, which gives the bridegroom (Bap.) an opportunity to meet the minister (Epis.) and have a nice, long chat about religion, while the best man (Atheist) talks to the eighty-three-year-old sexton who buried the bride's grandpa and grandma and has knowed little Miss Dorothy come twenty years next Michaelmas. The best man's offer of twenty-five dollars, if the sexton will at once bury the maid of honor, is generally refused as a matter of courtesy.

The bridal dinner

In the evening, the parents of the bride give the bridal dinner, to which all the relatives and close friends of the family are invited. Toasts are drunk in orange juice and rare old Virginia Dare wine, and much good-natured fun is indulged in by all. Speeches are usually made by the bride and groom, their parents, the best man, the maid of honor, the minister and Aunt Harriet.

Just a word about the speeches at a bridal dinner. Terrible!

A church wedding

On the day of the wedding the ushers should arrange to be at the church an hour or so in advance of the time set for the ceremony. They should be dressed in cutaways, with ties, gloves and gardenias provided by the groom.

It is the duty of the best man to dress the bridegroom for the wedding. As you enter his room you see, lying half-dressed on the bed, a pale, wan, emaciated creature, who is staring fixedly at the ceiling. It is the happy bridegroom. His lips open. He speaks feebly. "What time is it?" he says. You reply, "Two-thirty, old man. Time to start getting dressed." "Oh, my God!" says the groom. Ten minutes pass. "What time is it?" says the groom. "Twenty of three," you reply. "Here's your shirt." "Oh, my God!" says the groom.

He takes the shirt and tries to put it on. You help him. "Better have a little Scotch, old man," you say. "What time is it?" he replies. "Five of three," you say. "Oh, my God!" says the groom.

At three-thirty you and he are dressed in cutaways and promptly at three-forty-two you arrive at the church. You are ushered into a little side room where it is your duty to sit with the corpse for the few brief hours which elapse between three-forty-five and four o'clock. Occasionally he stirs and a faint spark of life seems to struggle in his sunken eyes. His lips move feebly. You bend over to catch his dying words. "Have you—got—the ring?" he whispers. "Yes," you reply. "Everything's fine. You look great, too, old man." The sound of the organ reaches your ears. The groom groans. "Have you got the ring?" he says.

Meanwhile the ushers have been performing their duty of showing the invited guests to the various pews. A correctly trained usher will always have ready some cheery word or sprightly bit of conversation to make the guests feel perfectly at home as he conducts them to their seats. "It's a nice day, isn't it?" is suggested as a perfectly safe and yet not too unusual topic of conversation. This can be varied by remarking, "Isn't it a nice day?" or in some cases, where you do not wish to appear too forward, "Is it a nice day, or isn't it?" An usher should also remember that although he has on a cutaway, he is neither a floor-walker nor a bond sales-man, and remarks such as "Something in a dotted Swiss?" or "Third aisle over—second pew—next the ribbon goods," are decidedly *non au fait*.

The first two pews on each side of the center aisle are always reserved for members of the immediate family, but it is a firmly established custom that the ushers shall seat in these "family pews" at least three people with whom the family are barely on speaking terms. This slight error always causes Aunt Nellie and Uncle Fred to sit up in the gallery with the family cook.

With the arrival of the bride, the signal is given to the organist to start the wedding march, usually either Mendelssohn's or Wagner's. About this time the mother of the bride generally discovers that the third candle from the left on the rear altar has not been lighted, which causes a delay of some fifteen minutes during which time the organist improvises one hundred and seventy-three variations on the opening strains of the march.

Finally all is adjusted and the procession starts down the aisle led by the ushers swaying slowly side by side. It is always customary for three or four of the eight ushers to have absolutely no conception of time or rhythm, which adds a quaint touch of uncertainty and often a little humor to the performance.

After the Scotch mist left by the passing ushers has cleared, there come the bridesmaids, the maid of honor, and then leaning on her father's arm (unless, of course, her father is dead), the bride.

In the meantime, the bridegroom has been carried in by the best man and awaits the procession at the foot of the aisle, which is usually four hundred and forty yards long. The ushers and bridesmaids step awkwardly to one side; the groom advances and a hush falls over the congregation which is the signal for the bride's little niece to ask loudly, "What's that funny looking man going to do, Aunt Dotty?"

Then follows the religious ceremony.

Immediately after the church service, a reception is held at the bride's home, where refreshments are served and two hundred and forty-two invited guests make the same joke about kissing the bride. At the reception it is customary for the ushers and the best man to crawl off in separate corners and die.

The wedding "festives" are generally concluded with the disappearance of the bride, the bridegroom, one of the uninvited guests and four of the most valuable presents.

THE CLICHÉ EXPERT TESTIFIES
ON THE DRAMA

✍ FRANK SULLIVAN

Q—Mr. Arbuthnot, you are an expert on the clichés of the drama, and in particular of drama criticism?

A—I am a battle-scarred veteran of not a few first nights.

Q—Then, with your permission, I shall test your competence in the field by putting a few questions to you.

A—Please do so.

Q—Where is Alexander Cohen?

A—Oh his way to London to secure the American rights.

Q—Excellent. And what did you think of *The Gay Mortician,* which opened at the Patricia Collinge Theatre last Monday night under the management of—

A—Please do not say "under the management." The correct phrase is "under the aegis." Well, in this reviewer's opinion *The Gay Mortician* was powerfully wrought, richly rewarding, utterly engaging, eminently satisfactory, wholly convincing, beautifully integrated, admirably played, and fairly obvious.

Q—In what way was it effective?

A—It was pictorially effective.

Q—How beautiful was it?

A—It was breathtakingly beautiful, and it was magnificently mounted.

Q—And how contrived?

A—Poorly contrived.

Q—I think you qualify, Mr. Arbuthnot. Tell me, as an expert in drama criticism, what would you say actors like Fredric March and Sir Laurence Olivier contribute?

A—They contribute masterly performances. They carry the major load. They do a grand job, give a good account of themselves, and make the most of. Not only that but their acting is incisive. Of course, they are supported.

Q—By what?

A—A competent cast.

Q—How?

A—Ably.

Q—I see. Now, in reference to that young actress who recently made such a hit in *Turnips at Nine-Thirty,* what did she do?

A—She stole the show.

Q—Stole it, eh? What does that mean?

A—It means she walked away with the evening's honors. She brought down the house.

Q—How?

A—By showing great promise, by captivating the audience, and by radiating charm. She leaped into popularity overnight. She skyrocketed to fame.

Q—Why?

A—Because she is pleasing to the eye and brings a rare and refreshing talent to the theatre.

Q—That indicates what?

A—It indicates that her name will soon be in lights. She will be elevated to stardom.

Q—I see. Tell me, Mr. Arbuthnot, what kind of roles do Lynn Fontanne and Helen Hayes play?

A—They play stellar roles.

Q—Why?

A—Because they are first ladies of the theatre, and great ladies of the stage.

Q—Why are they great ladies of the stage?

A—Because they are actresses of distinction.

Q—What kind of distinction?

A—Rare distinction.

Q—Now, when a great lady of the stage opens in a play—

A—Pardon me. Great ladies of the stage do not play in plays. They play in vehicles.

Q—Vehicles?

A—Yes. "Our Man Friday hears that Helen Hayes' *vehicle* for next season may be Elmer van Druten's new comedy drama, *The Sin of Leland Hayward.*"

Q—Now, then, when great ladies of the stage are in a cast—

A—They are never *in* a cast. They *grace* a cast.

Q—I beg your pardon. When they grace a cast, how do they act?

A—With emotional intensity, consummate artistry, and true awareness. They are superb as. They are magnificent in the role of. It is good to have them back.

Q—And how are their performances etched?

A—Finely. They have the ring.

Q—What ring?

A—The ring of authority. They bring new understanding to the role of Shakespeare's immortal heroine. They make the part come alive.

Q—I see. Now, Mr. Arbuthnot, when Thornton Sherwood writes a play—

A—Sir, the *mot juste* continues to elude you. Playwrights do not write plays. They fashion them.

Q—How?

A—With due respect for the eternal verities.

Q—How else?

A—With deft strokes, scalpel wit, loving care, penetrating insight, and masterly craftsmanship.

Q—Why?

A—So that Joshua Logan may direct the plays with authority and imagination.

Q—What kinds of plays are there?

A—Oh, their number is legion. There are dramas of frustration and dramas of extramarital love, or the eternal triangle. There are plays that are penetrating studies and plays that are valuable human documents. There are pageants, which ought to be glittering, if possible. Tragedies should, of course, be stark, and melodramas lurid, and spectacles, to be *de rigueur,* should be lavish, colorful, or handsome. But lampoons must be merry, farces must be rollicking, and comedies must be either of ancient vintage or sophisticated.

Q—What does the playwright do in a sophisticated comedy?

A—He pokes fun at our foibles. He dissects our tribal mores.

Q—Using what kind of vein?

A—A rich vein of satire.

Q—The task of the playwright sounds onerous enough, Mr. Arbuthnot

A—Oh, you have no idea of the angles he must consider. He must, for instance, make sure that his play has compelling moments. He must take care that it is well knit and fast-moving, and that it is brilliant in conception, builds up to an exciting climax, and ends on a happy note. Then, there is the character insight.

Q—What about that?

A—Well, he must provide plenty of it, along with a scope.

Q—Must have a scope, too, eh?

A—Yes, preferably wide.

Q—Why?

A—So that his play may provide a rich or rewarding experience. So that it may be first-rate entertainment, a major event of the theatrical season, and the most important contribution to the drama in years. In short, so that it may be a Must.

Q—Why must it be a Must?

A—If it isn't, it will rate as a disappointment and die a-borning.

Q—If the play is a comedy, how should it be packed?

A—With laughs, and it must be full of quiet humor.

Q—Any other kind of humor?

A—Yes, Adult. And it must be a lighthearted comedy.

Q—Why?

A—So it can be put down as the funniest play since. It held this reviewer.

Q—If it hadn't held this reviewer, what would have happened?

A—Then it would have left this reviewer cold. He must confess it.

Q—He must?

A—Yes. This reviewer must confess the play left him cold.

Q—Why?

A—Because it does not live up to the promise of the first act. Or it gets off to a slow start. It drags, peters out, and falls apart. It fails to convey.

Q—Are you insinuating that the plot—

A—Wears thin. Precisely. It is full of weak spots.

Q—What are *they*?

A—Structural defects. It also lacks spontaneity.

Q—What else does it lack?

A—Substance, drive, authority, emotional power, and oomph.

Q—The result being?

A—The result being that its charm eluded this reviewer. The opening-night reception was mixed.

Q—Why?

A—Because it doesn't quite come off, despite. Because it is handicapped by. This reviewer found it hackneyed, fustian, contrived, pedestrian, slim, meagre, talky, run-of-the-mill, uninspired, uneven, fumbling, dull, grim, confused, tedious, undistinguished, mediocre, routine, dreary, pretentious, slick, and pointless.

Q—You didn't like it?

A—It left much to be desired.

Q—If it had not left much to be desired, what would it have furnished?

A—It would have furnished an enchanting evening in the theatre, or a rare, memorable, interesting, or delightful evening in same. It would have been drama of a high order.

Q—You mean it would have been sheer magic?

A—Indeed yes. It had the first-nighters cheering.

Q—The blasé first-nighters?

A—Yes, and the veteran first-nighters, too. This reviewer thought it warm, whimsical, amusing in spots, clever, believable, gossamer, decorative, competent, unpretentious, witty, likeable, pleasant, literate, pat, engaging, winning, lilting, luminous, honest, captivating, and agreeable.

Q—That certainly is a quote to warm a press agent's heart, Mr. Arbuthnot.

A—Oh, it's nothing. It means I merely *liked* the play. That is, I thought it had its moments, if you care for that sort of thing. If I had *really* liked it, I should have found it masterly, brilliant, electric, terrific, inimitable, thrilling, dazzling, exciting, magnificent, riotous, splendid, uproarious, powerful, vivid, gripping, flawless—

Q—I see. Well, that gives us the idea. Now, then, Mr. Arbuthnot—

A—Don't try to throttle me. You asked for it, you know. Allow me to continue.

Q—All right, continue.

A—Where was I when you interrupted?

Q—Flawless.

A—Yes, flawless. Also authentic, dynamic, arresting, tense, absorbing, lavish, tender, provocative, poignant, superior, expert, melodious, sprightly, scintillating, haunting, and glowing.

Q—Mr. Arbuthnot, that's really a rave. You went overboard for that play.

A—I suppose you could say I did. Though, if I had really, *really* liked it, I'd have called it incandescent instead of glowing.

Q—In fine, would it be reasonable to infer that you thought the play a surefire antidote for the blues?

A—Oh, it is well worth seeing. Absolutely top-drawer, Grade A entertainment.

Q—And you envy whom?

A—I envy those seeing it for the first time. I recommend it heartily. No one can afford to pass it up. I loved every moment of it.

Q—Ranks with the best, eh?

A—It does indeed. Seldom has this reviewer beheld. Of course, it is no *South Pacific*. Bravura!

Q—Bravura?

A—Yes. "Bravura" is a mighty good word for a critic to have in his tool kit. Do you know what Jean Dalrymple plans?

Q—No. What?

A—She plans to present. And guess what Lillian Hellman is revising.

Q—The second act of her as yet untitled drama?

A—Oh, you spoiled it! You're not supposed to give the answers.

Q—I'm sorry. Well, here's one for you. What has Cheryl Crawford taken?

A—An option on.

Q—Right. And who must quit the cast on June 1st, because of prior commitments in Hollywood?

A—Rex Harrison.

Q—Right again. What has Arthur Miller completed?

A—The first draft.

Q—Now, Mr. Arbuthnot, let's conclude our session in a blaze of glory by tackling José Ferrer.

A—Oh, boy!

Q—Describe Mr. Ferrer's activities.

A—Well-l-l, let me see. José Ferrer presents, José Ferrer will produce, José Ferrer will star in, José Ferrer will co-star in, José Ferrer will film, José Ferrer has been inked, José Ferrer plans, José Ferrer records, José Ferrer will lecture, José Ferrer has been awarded, José Ferrer will broadcast, and José Ferrer is consider-ing.

Q—A perfectly brilliant summary, Mr. Arbuthnot, and I cannot tell you how grateful we all are to you for this enchanting excur-sion into—

A—The world of make-believe—right? Good. So long.

THE PRIVATE LIFE OF
MR. BIDWELL

✍ JAMES THURBER

From where she was sitting, Mrs. Bidwell could not see her hus-band, but she had a curious feeling of tension: she knew he was up to something.

"What are you doing, George?" she demanded, her eyes still on her book.

"Mm?"

"What's the matter with you?"

"Pahhhhh-h-h," said Mr. Bidwell, in a long, pleasurable exhale. "I was holding my breath."

Mrs. Bidwell twisted creakingly in her chair and looked at him; he was sitting behind her in his favorite place under the parch-ment lamp with the street scene of old New York on it. "I was just holding my breath," he said again.

"Well, please don't do it," said Mrs. Bidwell, and went back to her book. There was silence for five minutes.

"George!" said Mrs. Bidwell.

"Bwaaaaaa," said Mr. Bidwell. "What?"

"Will you please stop that?" she said. "It makes me nervous."

"I don't see how that bothers you," he said. "Can't I breathe?"

"You can breathe without holding your breath like a goop," said

Mrs. Bidwell. "Goop" was a word that she was fond of using; she rather lazily applied it to everything. It annoyed Mr. Bidwell.

"Deep breathing," said Mr. Bidwell, in the impatient tone he used when explaining anything to his wife, "is good exercise. You ought to take more exercise."

"Well, please don't do it around me," said Mrs. Bidwell turning again to the pages of Mr. Galsworthy.

At the Cowans' party, a week later, the room was full of chattering people when Mrs. Bidwell, who was talking to Lida Carroll, suddenly turned around as if she had been summoned. In a chair in a far corner of the room, Mr. Bidwell was holding his breath. His chest was expanded, his chin drawn in; there was a strange stare in his eyes, and his face was slightly empurpled. Mrs. Bidwell moved into the line of his vision and gave him a sharp, penetrating look. He deflated slowly and looked away.

Later, in the car, after they had driven in silence a mile or more on the way home, Mrs. Bidwell said, "It seems to me you might at least have the kindness not to hold your breath in other people's houses."

"I wasn't hurting anybody," said Mr. Bidwell.

"You looked silly!" said his wife. "You looked perfectly crazy!" She was driving and she began to speed up, as she always did when excited or angry. "What do you suppose people thought— you sitting there all swelled up, with your eyes popping out?"

"I wasn't all swelled up," he said, angrily.

"You looked like a goop," she said. The car slowed down, sighed, and came to a complete, despondent stop.

"We're out of gas," said Mrs. Bidwell. It was bitterly cold and nastily sleeting. Mr. Bidwell took a long, deep breath.

The breathing situation in the Bidwell family reached a critical point when Mr. Bidwell began to inhale in his sleep, slowly, and exhale with a protracted, growling "woooooooo." Mrs. Bidwell, ordinarily a sound sleeper (except on nights when she was sure burglars were getting in), would wake up and reach over and shake her husband. "George!" she would say.

"Hawwwwww," Mr. Bidwell would say, thickly. "Wahs maa nah, hm?"

After he had turned over and gone back to sleep, Mrs. Bidwell would lie awake, thinking.

One morning at breakfast she said, "George, I'm not going to put up with this another day. If you can't stop blowing up like a grampus, I'm going to leave you." There was a slight, quick lift in Mr. Bidwell's heart, but he tried to look surprised and hurt.

"All right," he said. "Let's not talk about it."

Mrs. Bidwell buttered another piece of toast. She described to him the ways he sounded in his sleep. He read the paper.

With considerable effort, Mr. Bidwell kept from inflating his chest for about a week, but one night at the McNallys' he hit on the idea of seeing how many seconds he could hold his breath. He was rather bored by the McNallys' party, anyway. He began timing himself with his wristwatch in a remote corner of the living-room. Mrs. Bidwell, who was in the kitchen talking children and clothes with Bea McNally, left her abruptly and slipped back into the living-room. She stood quietly behind her husband's chair. He knew she was there, and tried to let out his breath imperceptibly.

"I see you," she said, in a low, cold tone. Mr. Bidwell jumped up.

"Why don't you let me alone?" he demanded.

"Will you please lower your voice?" she said, smiling so that if anyone were looking he wouldn't think the Bidwells were arguing.

"I'm getting pretty damned tired of this," said Mr. Bidwell in a low voice.

"You've ruined my evening!" she whispered.

"You've ruined mine, too!" he whispered back. They knifed each other, from head to stomach, with their eyes.

"Sitting here like a goop, holding your breath," said Mrs. Bidwell. "People will think you are an idiot." She laughed, turning to greet a lady who was approaching them.

Mr. Bidwell sat in his office the next afternoon, a black, moist afternoon, tapping a pencil on his desk, and scowling. "All right, then, get out, get out!" he muttered. "What do I care?" He was visualizing the scene when Mrs. Bidwell would walk out on him. After going through it several times, he returned to his work, feeling vaguely contented. He made up his mind to breathe any way he wanted to, no matter what she did. And, having come to this decision, he oddly enough, and quite without effort, lost interest in holding his breath.

Everything went rather smoothly at the Bidwells' for a month or so. Mr. Bidwell didn't do anything to annoy his wife beyond leaving his razor on her dressing-table and forgetting to turn out the hall light when he went to bed. Then there came the night of the Bentons' party.

Mr. Bidwell, bored as usual, was sitting in a far corner of the room, breathing normally. His wife was talking animatedly with Beth Williamson about negligees. Suddenly her voice slowed and an uneasy look came into her eyes: George was up to something. She turned around and sought him out. To anyone but Mrs. Bidwell he must have seemed like any husband sitting in a chair. But his wife's lips set tightly. She walked casually over to him.

"What are you doing?" she demanded.

"Hm?" he said, looking at her vacantly.

"What are you *doing*?" she demanded again. He gave her a harsh, venomous look, which she returned.

"I'm multiplying numbers in my head," he said, slowly and evenly, "if you must know." In the prolonged, probing examination that they silently, without moving any muscles save those of their eyes, gave each other, it became solidly, frozenly apparent to both of them that the end of their endurance had arrived. The curious bond that held them together snapped—rather more easily than either had supposed was possible. That night, while undressing for bed, Mr. Bidwell calmly multiplied numbers in his head. Mrs. Bidwell stared coldly at him for a few moments, holding a stocking in her hand; she didn't bother to berate him. He paid no attention to her. The thing was simply over.

George Bidwell lives alone now (his wife remarried). He never goes to parties any more, and his old circle of friends rarely sees him. The last time that any of them did see him, he was walking along a country road with the halting, uncertain gait of a blind man: he was trying to see how many steps he could take without opening his eyes.

SONNY BOY

✍ P. G. WODEHOUSE

On the question of whether Bingo Little was ethically justified in bringing his baby into the club and standing it a milk straight in the smoking room, opinion at the Drones was sharply divided. A Bean with dark circles under his eyes said that it was not the sort of thing a chap wanted to see suddenly when he looked in for a drop of something to correct a slight queasiness after an exacting night. A more charitable Egg argued that as the child was presumably coming up for election later on, it was as well for it to get to know the members. A Pieface thought that if Bingo did let the young thug loose on the premises, he ought at least to give the Committee a personal guarantee for all hats, coats and umbrellas.

"Because if ever I saw a baby that looked like someone the police were spreading a dragnet for," said the Pieface, "it is this baby of Bingo's. Definitely the criminal type. It reminds me of Edward G. Robinson."

A Crumpet, always well informed, was able to throw a rather interesting light on the situation.

"I agree," he said, "that Algernon Aubrey Little is not a child whom I personally would care to meet down a dark alley, but Bingo assures me that his heart is in the right place, and as for his bringing him here and lushing him up, that is readily explained. He is grateful to this baby and feels that the best is none too good for it. By doing the right thing at the right time, it recently pulled him out of a very nasty spot. It is not too much to say, he tells me, that but for its intervention a situation would have been precipitated in his home life which might well have staggered humanity."

When in the second year of his marriage to Rosie M. Banks, the eminent female novelist, this union was blessed and this bouncing boy appeared on the London scene, Bingo's reactions (said the Crumpet) were, I gather, very much the same as yours. Introduced to the child in the nursing home, he recoiled with a startled "Oi" and as the days went by the feeling that he had run up against something red hot in no way diminished. The only thing that prevented a father's love from faltering was the fact that there was in his possession a photograph of himself at the same early age, in which he, too, looked like a homicidal fried egg. This proof that it was possible for a child, in spite of a rocky start, to turn eventually into a suave and polished boulevardier with finely chiselled features heartened him a good deal, causing him to hope for the best.

Meanwhile, however, there was no getting away from it that the little stranger was at the moment as pronounced a gargoyle as ever drained a bottle, and Bingo, finding that a horse of that name was running in the three-o'clock at Plumpton, had no hesitation in putting ten pounds on it to cop. Always on the lookout for omens from on high, he thought that this must have been what the child had been sent for.

The failure of Gargoyle to finish in the first six left him in a position of considerable financial embarrassment. The tenner which he had placed on its nose was the last one he had, and its loss meant that he would have to go a month without cigarettes, cocktails and those other luxuries which to the man of refinement are so much more necessary than necessities.

For there was no glittering prospect open to him of being able to touch the head of the house for a trifle to be going on with. Mrs. Bingo's last words, before leaving for Worcestershire some two weeks previously to see her mother through a course of treatment at the Droitwich brine baths, had contained a strong injunction to him not to bet in her absence; and any attempt on his part to palliate his action by showing that he had supposed himself to be betting on a certainty would, he felt, be badly received.

No, the cash, if it was to be raised, must be raised from some other source, and in these circumstances his thoughts, as they had so often done before, turned to Oofy Prosser. That it was never a simple task to get into Oofy's ribs, but one always calculated to test the stoutest, he would have been the first to concede. But it so happened that in the last few days the club's tame millionaire had shown himself unexpectedly friendly. On one occasion, going into the writing room to dash off a letter to his tailor which he hoped would lead to an appeasement, Bingo had found him there, busy on what appeared to be a poem; and Oofy, after asking him if he knew any good rhymes to "eyes of blue," had gone on to discuss the married state with him, giving it as his opinion that it was the only life.

The conclusion Bingo drew was that love had at last found Oofy Prosser, and an Oofy in love, he reasoned, might—nay, must —be an Oofy in a melting mood which would lead him to scatter the stuff in heaping handfuls. It was with bright confidence, accordingly, that he made his way to the block of flats in Park Lane where the other had his lair, and it was with a feeling that his luck was in that, reaching the front door, he met Oofy coming out.

"Oh, hullo, Oofy," he said. "Good morning, Oofy. I say, Oofy . . ."

I suppose years of being the official moneyed man of the Drones have given Oofy Prosser a sort of sixth sense. You might almost say that he is clairvoyant. Without waiting to hear more, he made a quick sideways leap, like an antelope spotting a tiger, and was off in a cab, leaving Bingo standing there considering how to act for the best.

Taking a line through stoats and weasels, he decided that the only thing to do was to continue doggedly on the trail, so he toddled off to the Savoy Grill, whither he had heard the driver being told to drive, and arriving there some twenty minutes later found Oofy in the lobby with a girl. It was with considerable pleasure that he recognized her as an old pal, with whom in his bachelor days he had frequently trodden the measure, for this enabled him to well-well-well and horn in. And once Bingo has horned in, he is not easy to dislodge. A few minutes later they were seated round a table and he was telling the wine waiter to be sure to take the chill off the claret.

It didn't occur to him at the time, but looking back, Bingo had a feeling that Oofy would have been just as pleased if he hadn't shown up. There was a sort of constraint at the meal. Bingo was all right. He prattled freely, too. It was just that Oofy seemed not quite to have got the party spirit. Silent. Distrait. Absent-minded. Inclined to fidget in his chair and drum on the tablecloth with his fingers.

After the coffee, the girl said well, she supposed she ought to be hareing to Charing Cross and catching her train—she, it appeared, being headed for a country-house visit in Kent. Oofy, brightening a little, said he would come and see her off. And Bingo, faithful to his policy of not letting Oofy out of his sight, said he would come too. So they all tooled along, and after the train had pulled out, Bingo, linking his arm in Oofy's, said:

"I say, Oofy, I wonder if you would do me a trifling favour."

Even as he spoke, he tells me, he seemed to notice something odd in his companion's manner. Oofy's eyes had a sort of bleak, glazed look in them.

"Oh?" he said distantly. "You do, do you? And what is it, my bright young limpet? What can I do for you, my adhesive old porous plaster?"

"Could you lend me a tenner, Oofy, old man?"

"No, I couldn't."

"It would save my life."

"There," said Oofy, "you have put your finger on the insuperable objection to the scheme. I see no percentage in your being alive. I wish you were a corpse, preferably a mangled one. I should like to dance on your remains."

Bingo was surprised.

"Dance on my remains?"

"All over them."

Bingo drew himself up. He has his pride.

"Oh?" he said. "Well, in that case, tinkerty-tonk."

The interview then terminated. Oofy hailed a cab, and Bingo returned to his Wimbledon home. And he had not been there long, when he was informed that he was wanted on the telephone. He went to the instrument and heard Oofy's voice.

"Hullo," said Oofy. "Is that you? I say, you remember my saying I would like to dance on your mangled remains?"

"I do."

"Well, I've been thinking it over—"

Bingo's austerity vanished. He saw what had happened. Shortly after they had separated, Oofy's better nature must have asserted itself, causing remorse to set in. And he was just about to tell him not to give it another thought, because we all say more than we mean in moments of heat, when Oofy continued.

"—thinking it over," he said, "and I would like to add, 'in hobnailed boots.' Good-bye."

It was a tight-lipped and pensive Bingo Little who hung up the receiver and returned to the drawing room where he had been tucking into tea and muffins. As he resumed the meal, the tea turned to wormwood and the muffins to ashes in his mouth. The thought of having to get through a solid month without cocktails and cigarettes gashed him like a knife.

And he was just wondering if it might not be best after all, to go to the last awful extreme of confessing everything to Mrs. Bingo, when the afternoon post came in, and there was a letter from her. And out of it, as he tore open the envelope, tumbled a ten-pound note.

Bingo tells me that his emotions at this moment were almost indescribable. For quite a while, he says, he remained motionless in his chair with eyes closed, murmuring "What a pal! What a helpmeet!" Then he opened his eyes and started to read the letter.

It was a longish letter, all about the people at the hotel and a kitten she had struck up an acquaintance with and what her mother looked like when floating in the brine bath and so on and so forth, and it wasn't till the end that the tenner got a mention. Like all women, Mrs. Bingo kept the big stuff for her postscript.

> "P. S." (she wrote) "I am enclosing ten pounds. I want you to go to the bank and open an account for little Algy with it. Don't you think it will be too sweet, him having his own little account and his own little wee passbook?"

I suppose if a fairly sinewy mule had suddenly kicked Bingo in the face, he might have a felt a bit worse—but not much. The letter fell from his nerveless hands. Apart from the hideous shock of finding that he hadn't clicked after all, he thoroughly disapproved of the whole project. Himself strongly in favour of sharing the wealth, it seemed to him that the last thing to place in the hands of an impressionable child was a little wee passbook, starting it off in life—as it infallibly must—with capitalistic ideas out of tune with the trend of modern enlightened thought. Slip a baby ten quid, he reasoned, and before you knew where you were you had got another Economic Royalist on your hands.

So uncompromising were his views on the subject that there was a moment when he found himself toying with the notion of writing back and telling Mrs. Bingo—in the child's best interests —that he had received a letter from her stating that she was enclosing ten pounds but that, owing doubtless to a momentary carelessness on her part, no ten pounds had arrived with it. However, he dismissed the idea—not because it was not good, but because something told him that it was not good enough. Mrs. Bingo was a woman who wrote novels about girls who wanted to be loved for themselves alone, but she was not lacking in astuteness.

He finished his tea and muffins, and then, ordering the perambulator, had the son and heir decanted into it and started off for a saunter on Wimbledon Common. Many young fathers, I believe, shrink from this task, considering that it lowers their prestige, but Bingo had always enjoyed it.

Today, however, the jaunt was robbed of all its pleasure by the brooding melancholy into which the sight of the child, lying there dumb and aloof with a thumb in its mouth, plunged him. Hitherto he had always accepted with equanimity the fact that it was impossible for there to be any real exchange of ideas between his offspring and himself. An occasional gurgle from the former and on his side a few musical chirrups had served to keep them in touch. But now the thought that they were separated by an impassable gulf, which no chirrups could bridge, seemed to him poignant and tragic to a degree.

Here, he reflected, was he, penniless—and there was the infant, rolling in the stuff—and absolutely no way of getting together and adjusting things. If only he could have got through to Algernon Aubrey the facts relating to his destitute condition, he was convinced that there would have been no difficulty about arranging a temporary loan. It was the old story of frozen assets, which as, everybody knows, is the devil of a business and stifles commerce at the source.

So preoccupied was he with these moody meditations that it was not immediately that he discovered that somebody was speaking his name. Then, looking up with a start, he saw that a stout man in a frock coat and a bowler hat had come alongside, wheeling a perambulator containing a blob-faced baby.

"Good evening, Mr. Little," he said, and Bingo saw that it was his bookie, Charles ("Charlie Always Pays") Pikelet, the man who acted as party of the second part in the recent deal over the horse Gargoyle.

Having seen him before only at race meetings—where, doubtless from the best motives, he affected chessboard tweeds and a white panama—he had not immediately recognized him.

"Why, hullo, Mr. Pikelet," he said.

He was not really feeling in the vein for conversation and would have preferred to be alone with his thoughts, but the other appeared to be desirous of chatting, and he was prepared to stretch a point to oblige him. The prudent man always endeavours to keep in with bookies.

"I didn't know you lived in these parts. Is that your baby?"

"Ah," said Charles Pikelet, speaking despondently. He gave a quick look into the interior of the perambulator to which he was attached, and winced like one who had seen some fearful sight.

"Kitchy-kitchy," said Bingo.

"How do you mean, kitchy-kitchy?" asked Mr. Pikelet, puzzled.

"I was speaking to the baby," explained Bingo. "A pretty child," he added, feeling that there was nothing to be lost by giving the man the old oil.

Charles Pikelet looked up, amazement in his eyes. "Pretty?"

"Well, of course," said Bingo, his native honesty compelling him to qualify the statement, "I don't say he—if it is a he—is a Robert Taylor or—if a she—a Lana Turner. Pretty compared with mine, I meant."

Again Charles Pikelet appeared dumbfounded.

"Are you standing there and telling me this baby of mine isn't uglier than that baby of yours?" he cried, incredulously.

It was Bingo's turn to be stunned.

"Are you standing there and telling me it is?"

"I certainly am. Why, yours looks human."

Bingo could scarcely believe his ears.

"Human? Mine?"

"Well, practically human."

"My poor misguided Pikelet, you're talking rot."

"Rot, eh?" said Charles Pikelet, stung. "Perhaps you'd care to have a bet on it? Five to one I'm offering that my little Arabella here stands alone as the ugliest baby in Wimbledon."

A sudden thrill shot through Bingo. No one has a keener eye than he for recognizing money for jam.

"Take a tenner?"

"Tenner it is."

"Okay," said Bingo.

"Kayo," said Charles Pikelet. "Where's your tenner?"

This introduction of a rather sordid note into the discussion caused Bingo to start uneasily.

"Oh, dash it," he protested, "surely elasticity of credit is the very basis of these transactions. Chalk it up on the slate."

Mr. Pikelet said he hadn't got a slate.

Bingo had to think quick. He had a tenner on his person, of course, but he realized that it was in the nature of trust money, and he had no means of conferring with Algernon Aubrey and ascertaining whether the child would wish to slip it to him. It might be that he had inherited his mother's lack of the sporting spirit.

And then, with quick revulsion, he felt that he was misjuding the little fellow. No son of his would want to pass up a snip like this.

"All right," he said. "Here you are."

He produced the note, and allowed it to crackle before Charles Pikelet's eyes.

"Right," said Charles Pikelet, satisfied. "Here's my fifty. And we'll put the decision up to this policeman that's coming along. Hoy, officer."

"Gents?" said the policeman, halting. He was a large, comfortable man with an honest face. Bingo liked the look of him, and was well content to place the judging in his hands.

"Officer," said Charles Pikelet, "to settle a bet, is this baby here uglier than that baby there?"

"Or vice versa?" said Bingo.

The policeman brooded over the two perambulators.

"They're neither of 'em to be compared with the one I've got at home," he said, a little smugly. "There's a baby with a face that would stop a clock. And the missus thinks it's a beauty. I've had many a hearty laugh over that," said the policeman, indulgently.

Both Charles Pikelet and Bingo felt that he was straying from the point.

"Never mind about your baby," said Charles Pikelet.

"No," said Bingo. "Stick closely to the res."

"Your baby isn't a runner," said Charles Pikelet. "Only the above have arrived."

Called to order, the policeman intensified his scrutiny. He looked from the one perambulator to the other, and then from the other perambulator to the one. And it suddenly came over Bingo like a cold douche that this hesitation could only mean one thing. It was not going to be the absurdly simple walkover which he had anticipated.

"M'm!" said the policeman.

"Ha!" said the policeman.

Bingo's heart stood still. It was now plain to him that there was to be a desperately close finish. But he tells me that he is convinced that his entry would have nosed home, had it not been for a bit of extraordinarily bad luck in the straight! Just as the policeman stood vacillating, there peeped through the clouds a ray of sunshine. It fell on Arabella Pikelet's face, causing her to screw it up in a hideous grimace. And at the same instant, with the race neck and neck, she suddenly started blowing bubbles out of the corner of her mouth.

The policeman hesitated no longer. He took Miss Pikelet's hand and raised it.

"The winnah!" he said. "But you ought to see the one I've got at home."

If the muffins which Bingo had for tea had turned to ashes in his mouth, it was nothing compared with what happened to the chump chop and fried which he had for dinner. For by that time his numbed brain, throwing off the coma into which it had fallen, really got busy pointing out to him the various angles of the frightful mess he had let himself into. It stripped the seven veils from the situation, and allowed him to see it in all its stark grimness.

Between Bingo and Mrs. Bingo there existed an almost perfect love. From the very inception of their union they had been like ham and eggs. But he doubted whether the most Grade-A affection could stand up against the revelation of what he had done this day. Look at his story from whatever angle you pleased, it remained one that reflected little credit on a young father and at the best must inevitably lead to "Oh, how could you?" 's. And the whole wheeze in married life, he had come to learn, was to give the opposite number as few opportunities of saying "Oh, how could you?" as possible.

And that story would have to be told. The first thing Mrs. Bingo would want to see on her return would be Algernon Aubrey's passbook, and from the statement that no such passbook existed to the final, stammering confession would be but a step. No wonder that as he sat musing in his chair after dinner the eyes were haggard, the face drawn and the limbs inclined to twitch.

He was just jotting down on the back of an envelope a few rough notes such as "Pocket picked" and "Took the bally thing out of my pocket on a windy morning and it blew out of my hand" and speculating on the chances of these getting by, when he was called to the telephone to take a trunk call and found Mrs. Bingo on the other end of the wire.

"Hullo," said Mrs. Bingo.

"Hullo," said Bingo.

"Oh, hullo, darling."

"Hullo, precious."

"Hullo, sweetie-pie."

"Hullo, angel."

"Are you there?" said Mrs. Bingo. "How's Algy?"

"Oh, fine."

"As beautiful as ever?"

"Substantially, yes."

"Have you got my letter?"

"Yes."

"And the ten pounds?"

"Yes."

"Don't you think it's a wonderful idea?"

"Terrific."

"I suppose it was too late to go to the bank today?"

"Yes."

"Well, go there tomorrow morning before you come to Paddington."

"Paddington?"

"Yes. To meet me. We're coming home tomorrow. Mother swallowed some brine this morning, and thinks she'd rather go and take the mud baths at Pistany instead. It's in Czechoslovakia."

At any moment less tense than the present one, the thought of Mrs. Bingo's mother being as far away as Czechoslovakia would have been enough to cause Bingo's spirits to soar. But now the news hardly made an impression on him. All he could think of was that the morrow would see Mrs. Bingo in his midst. And then the bitter reckoning.

"The train gets to Paddington about twelve. Mind you're there."

"I'll be there."

"And bring Algy."

"Right ho."

"Oh, and, Bingo. Most important. You know my desk?"

"Desk. Yes."

"Look in the middle top drawer."

"Middle top drawer. Right."

"I left the proofs of my Christmas story for *Woman's Home* there, and I've had a very sniffy telegram saying that they must have them tomorrow morning. So will you be an angel and correct them and send them off by tonight's post without fail? You can't miss them. Middle top drawer of my desk, and the title is 'Tiny Fingers.' And now I must go back to Mother. She's still coughing. Good-bye, darling."

"Good-bye, precious."

"Good-bye, lambkin."

"Good-bye, my dream rabbit."

Bingo hung up the receiver and made his way to the study. He found the proofs of "Tiny Fingers," and taking pencil in hand seated himself at the desk and started in on them.

His heart was heavier than ever. Normally, the news that his mother-in-law had been swallowing brine and was still coughing would have brought a sparkle to his eyes and a happy smile to his lips, and now it left him cold. He was thinking of the conversation which had just concluded and remembering how cordial Mrs. Bingo's voice had been, how cheery, how loving—so absolutely in all respects the voice of a woman who thinks her husband a king among men. How different from the flat, metallic voice which was going to say "What!" to him in the near future.

And then suddenly, as he brooded over the galley slips, a sharp thrill permeated his frame and he sat up in his chair as if a new, firm backbone had been inserted in place of the couple of feet of spaghetti he had been getting along with till now. In the middle of slip two the story had started to develop, and the way in which it developed caused hope to dawn again.

I don't know if any of you are readers of Mrs. Bingo's output. If not, I may inform you that she goes in pretty wholeheartedly for the fruitily sentimental. This is so even at ordinary times, and for a Christmas number, of course, she naturally makes a special effort. In "Tiny Fingers" she had chucked off the wraps completely. Scooping up snow and holly and robin redbreasts and carol-singing villagers in both hands, she had let herself go and given her public the works.

Bingo, when I last saw him, told me the plot of "Tiny Fingers" in pitiless detail, and all I need touch on now is its main theme. It was about a hardhearted godfather who had given his goddaughter the air for marrying the young artist, and they came right back at him by shoving the baby under his nose on Christmas Eve—the big scene, of course, being the final one, where the old buster sits in his panelled library, steadying the child on his knee with one hand while writing a whacking big cheque with the other. And the reason it made such a deep impression on Bingo was that he had suddenly remembered that Oofy Prosser was Algernon Aubrey's godfather. And what he was asking himself was, if this ringing-in-the-baby wheeze had worked with Sir Aylmer Mauleverer, the hardest nut in the old-world village of Meadowvale, why shouldn't it work with Oofy?

It was true that the two cases were not exactly parallel, Sir Aylmer having had snow and robin redbreasts to contend against and it now being the middle of June. It was true, also, that Oofy, when guardedly consenting to hold the towel for Algernon Aubrey, had expressly stipulated that there must be no funny business and that a small silver mug was to be accepted in full settlement. Nevertheless, Bingo went to bed in optimistic mood. Indeed, his last thought before dropping off to sleep was a speculation as to whether, if the baby played his cards right, it might not be possible to work Oofy up into three figures.

He had come down a bit in his budget, of course, by the time he set out for Park Lane next morning. One always does after sleeping on these things. As he saw it now, twenty quid was about what it ought to pan out at. This, however, cut fifty-fifty between principal and manager, would be ample. He was no hog. All he wanted was to place child and self on a sound financial footing, and as he reached Oofy's flat and pressed the bell, he was convinced that the thing was in the bag.

In a less sanguine frame of mind, he might have been discouraged by the fact that the infant was looking more than ever like some mass-assassin who has been blackballed by the Devil's Island Social and Outing Club as unfit to associate with the members, but his experience with Charles Pikelet and the policeman had shown him that this was how all babies of that age looked, and he had no reason to suppose that the one in "Tiny Fingers" had been any different. The only thing Mrs. Bingo had stressed about the latter had been its pink toes, and no doubt Algernon Aubrey, if called upon to do so, could swing as pink a toe as the next child. It was with bright exuberance that he addressed Oofy's man, Corker, as he opened the door.

"Oh, hullo, Corker. Lovely morning. Mr. Prosser in?"

Corker did not reply immediately. The sight of Algernon Aubrey seemed momentarily to have wiped speech from his lips. Perfectly trained valet though he was, he had started back on perceiving him, his arms raised in a rudimentary posture of self-defense.

"Yes, sir," he replied, at length. "Mr. Prosser is at home. But he is not yet up, sir. He was out late last night."

Bingo nodded intelligently. Oofy's practice of going out on the tiles and returning with the morning milk was familiar to him.

"Ah well," he said tolerantly. "Young blood, Corker, eh?"

"Yes, sir."

"It's a poor heart that never rejoices."

"So I have been informed, sir."

"I'll just pop in and pip-pip."

"Very good, sir. Shall I take your luggage?"

"Eh? Oh no, thanks. This is Mr. Prosser's godson. I want them to meet. This'll be the first time he's seen him."

"Indeed, sir?"

"Rather make his day, what?"

"So I should be disposed to imagine, sir. If you will follow me, sir. Mr. Prosser is in the sitting room."

"In the sitting room? I thought you said he was in bed."

"No, sir. On his return home this morning, Mr. Prosser appears to have decided not to go to bed. You will find him in the fireplace."

And so it proved. Oofy Prosser was lying with his head on the fender and his mouth open. He wore an opera hat and what would have been faultless evening dress if he had a tie on instead of a blue ribbon of the sort which the delicately nurtured use to bind up their hair. In one hand he was clutching a pink balloon, and across his shirt front was written in lipstick the word "Whoops." His whole aspect was so plainly that of a man whom it would be unwise to stir that Bingo, chewing a thoughtful lip, stood pondering on what was the best policy to pursue.

It was a glance at his watch that decided him. He saw that he had been running rather behind schedule, and that if he was to meet Mrs. Bingo at Paddington at twelve-five he would have to be starting at once.

"This, Corker," he said to Corker, "has made things a bit complex, Corker. I've got to be at Paddington in ten minutes, and everything seems to point to the fact that Mr. Prosser, if roused abruptly, may wake up cross. Better, I think, to let him have his sleep out. So here is the procedure, as I see it. I will leave this baby on the floor beside him, so that they can get together in due course, and I will look in and collect it on my way back."

"Very good, sir."

"Now, Mr. Prosser's first move, on waking and finding the place crawling with issue, will no doubt be to ring for you and ask what it's all about. You will then say, 'This is your godson, sir.' You couldn't manage 'itsy-bitsy godson,' could you?"

"No, sir."

"I was afraid not. Still, you've got the idea of the thing? Good. Fine. Right ho."

The train from Droitwitch was rolling in just as Bingo came onto the platform, and a moment later he spotted Mrs. Bingo getting out. She was supporting her mother who still seemed rocky on the pins, but on seeing him she detached herself from the old geezer, allowing her to navigate temporarily under her own steam, and flung herself into his arms.

"Bingo, darling!"

"Rosie, my pre-eminent old egg!"

"Well, it is nice being back with you again. I feel as if I had been away years. Where's Algy?"

"I left him at Oofy Prosser's. His godfather, you know. I had a minute or two spare on my way here, so I looked in on Oofy. He was all over the child and just wouldn't let him go. So I arranged that I would call for him on my way back."

"I see. Then I had better meet you there after I've taken Mother to her flat. She's not at all well."

"No, I noticed she seemed to be looking a bit down among the wines and spirits," said Bingo, casting a gratified glance at the old object, who was now propping herself up against a passing porter. "The sooner you get her off to Czechoslovakia, the better. All right, then. See you at Oofy's."

"Where does he live?"

"Bloxham Mansions, Park Lane."

"I'll be there as soon as I can. Oh, Bingo, darling, did you deposit that money for Algy?"

Bingo struck his forehead.

"Well, I'm dashed! In the excitement of meeting you, my dream of joy, I clean forgot. We'll do it together after leaving Oofy."

Brave words, of course, but as he hiked back to Bloxham Mansions, there suddenly came on him for the first time an unnerving feeling of doubt as to whether he was justified in taking it for granted that Oofy would come across. At the moment when he had conceived the scheme of using Algernon Aubrey as a softening influence, he had felt that it was a cinch. It had taken only about five minutes of his godson's society to bring the milk of human kindness sloshing out of Sir Aylmer Mauleverer in bucketfuls, and he had supposed that the same thing would happen with Oofy. But now there began to burgeon within him a chilling uncertainty, which became intensified with every step he took.

It had just occurred to him that Algernon Aubrey was up against a much stiffer proposition than the child in "Tiny Fingers." Sir Aylmer Mauleverer had been a healthy, outdoor man, the sort that springs from bed and takes a hearty breakfast. There had been no suggestion, as far as he could remember, of his having a morning head. Oofy, on the other hand, it was only too abundantly evident, was going to have, when he awoke to face a new day, a morning head of the first water. Everything, he realized, turned on how that head would affect a godfather's outlook.

It was with tense anxiety that he demanded hot news from Corker as the door opened.

"Any developments, Corker?"

"Well, yes and no, sir."

"How do you mean, yes and no? Has Mr. Prosser rung?"

"No, sir."

"Then he's still asleep?"

"No, sir."

"But you said he hadn't rung."

"No, sir. But a moment ago I heard him utter a cry."

"A cry?"

"Yes, sir. A piercing cry, indicative of a considerable distress of mind. It was in many respects similar to his ejaculation on the morning of January the first of the present year, on the occasion when he supposed—mistakenly—that he had seen a pink elephant."

Bingo frowned.

"I don't like that."

"Nor did Mr. Prosser, sir."

"I mean, I don't like the way things seem to have been shaping. You're a man of the world, Corker. You know as well as I do that godfathers don't utter piercing cries on meeting their godsons, unless there is something seriously amiss. I think I'll step along and take a rekko."

He did so and, entering the sitting room and noting contents, halted with raised eybrows.

Algernon Aubrey was sitting on the floor, his attention riveted on the balloon, which he appeared to be trying to swallow. Oofy Prosser was standing on the mantel-piece, gazing down with bulging eyes. Bingo is a pretty shrewd sort of chap, and it didn't take him long to see that there was a sense of strain in the atmosphere. He thought the tactful thing to do was to pass it off as if one hadn't noticed anything.

"Hullo, Oofy," he said.

"Hullo, Bingo," said Oofy.

"Nice morning," said Bingo.

"Wonderful weather we're having," said Oofy.

They chatted for a while about the prospects for Hurst Park and the latest mid-European political developments, and then there was a pause. It was Oofy who eventually broke it.

"Tell me, Bingo," he said, speaking with a rather overdone carelessness, "I wonder if by any chance you can see anything on the floor, just over there by the fireplace. I daresay it's only my imagination, but it seems to me—"

"Do you mean the baby?"

Oofy gave a long sort of whistling gasp.

"It is a baby? I mean, you can see it, too?"

"Oh, rather. With the naked eye," said Bingo. "Pipsywipsy," he added, lugging the child into the conversation so that he wouldn't feel out of it. "Dada can see you."

Oofy started.

"Did you say 'Dada'?"

" 'Dada' was the word."

"Is this your baby?"

"That's right."

"The little blighter I gave that silver mug to?"

"None other."

"What's he doing here?"

"Oh, just paying a social call."

"Well," said Oofy, in an aggrieved voice, starting to climb down, "if he had the sense to explain that at the outset, I would have been spared a terrible experience. I came in a bit late last night and sank into a refreshing sleep on the floor, and I woke to find a frightful face glaring into mine. Naturally, I thought the strain had been too much and that I was seeing things."

"Would you like to kiss your godson?"

Oofy shuddered strongly.

"Don't say such things, even in fun," he begged.

He reached the floor and stood staring at Algernon Aubrey from a safe distance.

"And to think," he murmured, "that I thought of getting married!"

"Marriage is all right," argued Bingo.

"True," Oofy conceded, "up to a certain point. But the risk! The fearful risk! You relax your vigilance for a second, you turn your head for a single instant, and—bing!—something like that happens."

"Popsy-wopsy," said Bingo.

"It's no good saying 'popsy-wopsy'—it's appalling. Bingo," said Oofy, speaking in a low, trembling voice, "do you realize that, but for your muscling in on that lunch of mine, this might have happened to me? Yes," he went on, paling beneath his pimples, "I assure you, I was definitely planning to propose to that girl over the coffee and cigarettes. And you came along and saved me." He drew a deep breath. "Bingo, old chap, don't I seem to recall hearing you ask me for a fiver or something?"

"A tenner."

Oofy shook his head.

"It's not enough," he said. "Would you mind if I made if fifty?"

"Not a bit."

"Or, rather, a hundred. You've no objection?"

"None whatever, old man."

"Good," said Oofy.

"Fine," said Bingo.

"Excuse me, sir," said Corker, appearing in the doorway, "the hall porter has rung up to say that Mrs. Little is waiting for Mr. Little downstairs."

"Tell her I'll be there in two ticks, with bells on," said Bingo.